6 17

LAWYER, HEAL THYSELF!

LAWYER, HEAL THYSELF!

by

BILL MORTLOCK

LONDON
VICTOR GOLLANCZ LTD
1959

Printed in Great Britain by
The Camelot Press Ltd., London and Southampton

CONTENTS

The product of an infinite series of integers of whatsoever magnitude is, if there be included in the series nought, nought also.

PROLOGUE

Even now it makes me laugh in spite of everything, when I catch a glimpse of myself ordering my private universe. But it's real all right. I spend my time poking my nose into other people's lives, fishing out from limbo the half-forgotten responses to unhappy situations. I get paid for it too. It must be so interesting, people say. You must get to know so much about people, they say, as if getting to know about people was simply bound to be interesting. But they use the wrong word.

It has its points of course. Living other people's lives saves me from my own. Or at any rate, it saves me from living my own life in the rather extreme way I have noticed in others. But even apart from that, there is, I think, a good deal to be said for vicarious living.

I didn't start off like this. I never really thought I was going to wind up as a universal mother and even then Willie Vincent had to tell me before I knew. I thought I was just going to be a lawyer. Not that I wanted to be a lawyer much, but when I came out of the Army I was twenty-seven, a husband and father and the only training I'd had except in murder was in Law and I'd got that before I'd been old enough to object. The responsible thing for me to do was to take my final examination and become a solicitor. I decided to be responsible. I had never consciously been responsible before. For all those twenty-seven years I had just let it all come at me and worked out the answers or ducked as I went along.

I got a job as an assistant in a firm of solicitors. They paid me £8 a week, though they called it £400 a year. It is after all a profession. It was a one-man firm and the one man was a fat fellow who'd sat tight in his office throughout the war. He had a multitude of clerks and typists and he kept his bookkeeper-cashier in a cage, as if Chesterton had never lived. I was his first qualified assistant and he was puffed up with pride about it, though he paid me less than the bookkeeper-cashier in the cage. But then I wasn't handling the firm's money.

The one man acted for a number of property speculators. I had never knowingly met a speculator but I had of course been rather sheltered since virtually the whole of my adult life had been spent in the Army. And you can't really count the selling of Army petrol and rations to civilians or the barter of chocolate and cigarettes for occupied women. That's rather different.

On the morning when I was to meet my first property speculator, I was filled with trepidation. I could see him entering the room. Fatly enclosed in a dark double-breasted suit, blue shaved jowls squeezed out of a stiff white collar, he would with a moist palm grip my hand and a loud voice would exercise dominion over me. With bogus bonhomie—"Nice room you have here"— he would proffer a friendly equality but beneath the rich ooze of his words, menace would subtly be underwritten.

A tiny, thin, rather dirty man was shown into my room. I looked at him unbelievingly. No double-breasted suit, no jowls and quite obviously no bonhomie. We did not shake hands. He looked to me as if he'd been dehydrated. And as at this time dehydrated vegetables were coming on to the market in enormous quantities, a terrible panicky thought ran through my head. I cleared my throat, braced my legs against the back of my chair and stood up to receive him. When he spoke, his voice was as diminished as the rest of him. I could hardly believe that speculation did this to a man.

But he was a speculator all right. I subsequently met a number of them and they all looked rather the same; harried little men, not at all as I had imagined, like High Priests using Society as their altar with the blood and guts of their victims thrown all over the stage. They were in fact rather boring men. Also, I simply couldn't understand what they were up to. I knew of course that the theory of speculation is that you make a lot of money, but the speculators I acted for only got ulcers. That may have been my fault and I dare say there are great Nabobs who do acquire vast fortunes by speculating in property. But I never met any of them. The ones I met spent their days wringing their hands, looking for buyers. And the buyers always seemed to change their minds just before the contract was signed.

My first speculator was called Buck. He had bought a block of flats and offices for £90,000. Naturally, he hadn't got £90,000.

He'd had to borrow £9,000 to pay the deposit and then he searched frantically for a month to borrow the rest. He finally got it at 12% repayable in 9 months.

I count those nine months as about the worst in my life and I have been through war, famine and pestilence. At the beginning, Buck started off full of hope to sell his block for £150,000. After three months and no buyers, his price dropped to £125,000. After six months the only offer he'd had was £80,000. In the last three months he aged ten years. He began to drop in to see me every day. And gradually his sense of failure began to clothe me also. We both knew he would have to sell at a huge loss; we could talk about nothing else. But the one subject we never mentioned was what he would do after his ruin was accomplished. We knew of course that he would have to kill himself. There was no point in discussing that. But the strain told. He couldn't get any thinner, but I could and did. Yet although he remained the same physical shape, he somehow seemed to be getting thinner inside as if his juices were dribbling away.

During the last month we were only able to talk in whispers. I did no work and Buck was in my room nearly all day. Nobody came near us, the telephone never rang, nothing happened. And the only sounds to be heard were Buck whispering to me and me whispering to Buck. We were about as close to the end of the world as anybody can get. Then suddenly an offer of £102,000 turned up. Miraculously we returned to life. I played that purchaser as no angler ever played a fish and when the day came that contracts were actually exchanged, I wept.

We managed to complete the sale just before the nine months ran out. And after we'd paid everybody out and deducted our costs, Buck had made £400. He had spent about a year buying and selling the property so that you could fairly say that he'd earned £8 a week. But he was delighted. It was when he began to prowl about for his next venture, that I decided to leave. I couldn't cope with that kind of life.

Then I got a job in an enlightened industrial company. It was really just a big factory. But you weren't allowed to call it that. You had to call it the Company and it took itself very seriously. The enlightened management hired me as a legal adviser. The Personnel Manager, known throughout the Company as the P.M., was also enlightened. He liked having what he called frank talks. The first day I arrived he had a frank talk with me. Previously, he said, they had employed a barrister to be their legal adviser and when he had left to get married—oh no, the P.M. said, he was a man, but he'd married a wealthy family—they had taken advice. The advice they got was that as a solicitor has to have a practical training in an office and to pass fairly stiff examinations and a barrister misses both these advantages, it would be better for the Company to employ a solicitor. Although the Board had been unwilling to lose the prestige of employing a barrister, in the end, he said, they had faced up to the fact. The P.M. looked at me hard and I coughed. It was clear that I was the fact they had faced up to.

The P.M. went on being frank. The Company, he said, employed several doctors and a dentist to look after the health and teeth of the workers, but the Board thought that the Company also needed a lawyer to solve the men's personal problems. In spite of so much frankness, what the P.M. did not tell me was that in the days before the War when the Company was still known as the factory, it had had a dreadful record of strikes and lock-outs and they were now doing everything they could to make everybody forget about it. He also didn't tell me that the Works Manager and half a dozen foremen still maintained the factory's pre-war attitudes and because it had been tough for them, they intended to see that it remained tough for everybody else. Perhaps he didn't know, but everybody else seemed to know, that every enlightened scheme proposed by the Management stopped at a level somewhere between Works Manager and foremen. If the Company had decided for example that it would be good for the men to drink a pint of milk at ten o'clock, the Works Manager and his foremen would soon have begun to look like cows rather than have allowed a drop of milk to be spilt on the benches below them. The result was that the labour relations record of the Company in terms of hostility and strikes was about the same as the record of the factory.

I once tried to explain all this to the P.M. I said I wanted to have a frank talk with him. He heard me out and then gave me a lecture on loyalty. I never tried again.

I was there about a year. In that time I sold a house for the General Manager, advised one of the girls in the typing pool (Management) about an action for breach of promise, discussed with the Sales Manager and the Principal Medical Officer whether Law was more rewarding professionally and materially than medicine and explained about twice a week to the Technical Manager that there was nothing he could lawfully do to prevent his daughter of 23 from marrying a Pole. This last series of conferences came to an end when I finally lost patience and suggested that if he went on obstructing the marriage, the almost certain consequence would be disastrous to his honour and to his house. He was the kind of man to whom one talks about his honour and his house. Once when a member of the Royal Family had come to visit the Company, I was standing by him and heard him intone with great feeling, "God bless you, Marm". He never came near me again.

I also read all of about 6,000 National Insurance (Industrial Injuries) Act regulations. But that wasn't the reason why I left. In the whole of my year with the Company not one of the 8,000 workers ever came near me for advice. I remember thinking it was a bit odd. But I never discovered till years later what had happened. And really it was all so simple. A man couldn't leave his bench without permission. The Works Manager and his foremen let it be known to the charge hands that permission granted to a man wanting to seek advice from the tame lawyer would incur their displeasure. And if a man were so anxious to get advice as to appeal to his shop steward for help, the shop steward would counsel him to see the Union lawyer. "You know where you are with your own people."

But during my year I finally persuaded myself that the Company's workers were a bunch of exceptionally well-behaved and well-integrated people who never moved house, never quarrelled and lived quiet grey eternal lives.

Much later, when I was in private practice I happened to call on a Solicitor who practised in the small town on the outskirts of which the Company stands and in which the workers live. He appeared to be prosperous enough and after we had done our business together, I said to him tentatively: "Are you busy here?" For answer, he swept his arm around his room. There were files everywhere. I said "Really?" He leaned forward and said confidentially: "Most of my work comes from the Company outside the town." "But," I interjected, "haven't they got their own legal staff?"

13

"Tcha," he replied contemptuously. "I don't act for the Company. It's the men. A magnificent lot they are. There are two firms of solicitors in this place and those men could, and sometimes do, keep us going without anything else." He shifted comfortably in his chair. "Everything," he said, "absolutely everything," and then in a reflective tone, he went on, "You see, they're a randy lot so we're never short of divorce; then they're always on the move and the Company has a huge turnover of labour, so we're always seeing new faces. There's everything," he repeated, "everything from rape to running down."

It was partly the boredom which finally drove me away. But it was also the bigness. It took six months to get a decision from the Board on almost anything. It was part of my job to advise the Board on small internal legal matters. All the important Company matters were sent straight to their solicitors without coming near me. But occasionally I was asked to advise on a Trade Union Agreement. My advice had to be put into writing with a myriad copies and then it was all handed to the P.M. who referred it to the Board. And nothing was ever heard again. No gods who dwelt on Olympus could have been invested with such authority as this Board. Everything had to be referred to them and once referred, you might just as well go into hibernation for the season. When I protested at first timidly and then savagely, the P.M. talked frankly of the Company's size. "You must remember that the Board can't just consider it from your point of view; they have to weigh it up from all points of view."

I began to spend the days choked with anger and frustration. I had never seen the Board, they never seemed to do anything, but the weight of their inertia clogged the whole of my life. Sometimes I doubted whether the Board even existed. I wondered how the factory functioned at all, ground between the mills of the Works Manager and those of the Board. But it was really Jakeman's feet which forced me out.

I had had a pretty gritty morning arguing with the P.M. over the draft of the latest agreement with one of the two Unions recognised by the Management. There were altogether sixteen Unions to which different sections of the men belonged but the Management only recognised two of them and that was that. There were constant strikes, fights and disturbances, all of which might have been ended if the fourteen unrecognised Unions had been recognised. Every week I submitted memoranda with the appropriate number of copies urging recognition. Every week the P.M. promised to refer my recommendation to the Board. And then there was a great silence. In the meantime the strikes went on.

I had shown the P.M. my draft. I thought it set out clearly and simply all the terms which had been agreed. He said that it would have to go to the Board for approval. I pointed out that the Union wouldn't wait six months, that the terms arrived at had been within the Board's directive and urged him to sign it on behalf of the Management there and then. He wouldn't agree, so I stalked out threateningly, pausing by his door to prophesy: "We'll have another strike on our hands if you won't take the responsibility."

In the afternoon while I was coming to the end of the sixth thousand of the National Insurance (Industrial Injuries) Act regulations, the P.M. came in and told me frankly that he was (on his own authority) giving me an assistant, Jakeman, who'd been there 25 years. I knew that men who'd been employed by the Company for 25 years were given special treatment and were virtually incapable of being sacked, whatever they did or did not do. Jakeman as a special mark of favour was to be my assistant. They didn't actually expect him to do anything, the P.M. said frankly. They just wanted to give him a place to sit and make him feel he still belonged. After all, he said, apparently without irony, to have stayed 25 years with the Company was something.

Even after a year, as the P.M. closed my door, I thought highly of these excellent sentiments. I welcomed Jakeman and gave him simple things to do, trying to make him feel he belonged. I got him to put the Statutory Instruments in the right order. Nobody ever looked at them and I didn't really care what he did with them.

But he had smelly feet. Once when people had talked to me of B.O. and sweaty armpits, there was a time in my life when I would have laughed airily. But not after Jakeman's feet. I began to find it impossible to breathe while he was in the room. I sent him on strange errands designed to keep him out all day and then hastily threw open the windows. But he said that he couldn't manage the walking and the errands had to stop. I suggested persuasively to him that as short walks tired his feet, he should see the doctors. He was an affable fellow and readily agreed. I briefed the doctors privily but their verdict was that short of amputating his feet, they were always going to smell because he didn't wash them. Finally I complained to the P.M.: "Jakeman," he replied "has been here 25 years." I began to see why the Board never made an appearance. But my position was weaker so I left.

Later, I wondered whether Jakeman's feet had been a trick to edge me out. I have never been able to make sure but I heard recently that they've gone back to barristers. I suppose I was not really a fact they liked facing up to.

Nearly three years had gone since I had left the Army, but speculators and sweaty feet had driven me naked and rather afraid to face a hostile world. On all sides my Army friends were succeeding—in the family business, in Government service, in advertising or in the City. They formed Companies, drove about in fast cars, discussed their expense accounts and complained about the Government. I accepted them at their own valuation. I see now that this was a mistake but the recognition has created its own confusion, because now I can never be sure that my own valuation of myself isn't as false as theirs. But at the time I accepted their estimate of their high quality. And my own failure made my mouth feel perpetually rank.

Growing up between the Wars as I did, I felt that an unemployed man should leave the house just after first light and tramp the streets looking for work. This was an impulse which I found it impossible to subdue rationally. I knew perfectly well that solicitors don't wait outside factories for work but the knowledge did nothing to allay the discomfort. In fact there were plenty of jobs to be had. They were advertised in the *Times* and the Law Society had its own employment register. All I needed to do was to write letters. And I did. But I never stopped feeling guilty. I shouldn't have been lying about comfortably in a house when I was out of work.

I made a bad showing at interviews because my record was so unfortunate—six years in the Army, two jobs in less than three years, thirty years of age and very little practical experience in a Solicitor's office. And I wasn't just looking for a job, I was seeking a partnership. I had no money to pay for it, no influential clients, and no backing of any kind. At night I began to dream about speculators with smelly feet.

I avoided the larger and older firms. Even if I could have found the money to pay for a partnership, it would have been years before I would have had anything like a free hand. Every morning the senior partner would have had me on parade with the other partners in his room and given us our instructions for the day. I wanted no more of that. I had done my stint for six long years.

I also avoided the people who exist on the edge of the profession; and the Solicitors who are really business men in their own right; and the fussy little men who live and work in one room at the top of high buildings, doing the typing with one hand and cooking the breakfast with the other. The result was rather depressing. There was hardly anybody left with whom I would consent to work.

I have two children. Edward is two years younger than Michael. Michael's sixth birthday took place during my unemployment, and the money was already beginning to run out. But I had to buy him a birthday present and one evening as I was talking about it to Mary my wife, I suddenly knew that I would buy him a very large Meccano set. Mary laughed. "Michael won't even be able to use the screw-driver," she said. I knew she was right but I bought it just the same. And I felt an odd triumph that I should have bought it when every penny was precious. It was one way of getting my own back.

One of the deepest frustrations of my childhood was that I had never been able to make anything which worked with my Meccano set. My friends of those days had made elaborate models which performed the most extraordinary feats. But mine never worked, not even when I had followed all the directions and it all looked right.

As I grew up, I forgot about this incapacity for nearly twenty years, until the week before Michael's birthday. Then came the great day. After much skimming through the instructional book, we all decided to make a highly complicated crane. The children had to go to bed long before it was finished, but at four o'clock in the morning it was done and to my surprise I found that it worked and that all the parts that were supposed to move, moved. Unemployed or not, I felt magnificent, even at that hour; I was a creator of the first rank.

Days then followed when I hardly stirred from the house. I just made cranes, gantry cranes, elevated jib cranes, hammerhead

17

cranes, breakdown cranes, derrick cranes, cranes of all kinds.

One week-end, I decided that now I had achieved my aim, I would make just one more crane and then hand the set over to Michael. By Sunday afternoon it was done, a beautiful travelling crane, and the children were playing with it. Relaxed, watching it work, no longer expecting it not to work, I was lying back in my chair and admitting to Mary that I would have to take the next job that offered. Not that so many were offered, but it was a lazy Sunday afternoon and I didn't want to lower our morale. I also didn't want again to have to counter her gentle complaint that most people who didn't like their jobs stayed in them, until they had found more congenial alternatives.

"This is the best crane you ever made Daddy," said Michael.

"No, I think the last one was better," countered Edward. "It was bigger."

"Because it was bigger doesn't make it better, does it Daddy?" Michael objected. A difficult problem this, I thought, the division between the old world and the new. I also thought of the Company and how bigness appeared to prevent decisions but it might equally well have been Jakeman's feet. I tried to be neutral.

"Well," I said officially, "bigness by itself doesn't make anything better, unless of course you like big things when I suppose bigness does make something better. And if you like small things then I expect you'd think that bigness makes things worse." I stopped, feeling rather fatuous. They had asked for an opinion, for some kind of standard and I had behaved like a lawyer giving them alternatives. Mary laughed:

"You've been off duty now for some time dear," she said.

I felt the anger rising in me against her for my stupidity, when the telephone rang.

"Do you want a job?" she said when she came back.

"What do you mean?" I asked.

"It's Dick Richards on the telephone."

"No, I know about that. It's his uncle. I met him some time ago. He wants a partner but it's in the provinces. I don't want to leave London if I can help it."

"I think perhaps you'd better talk to him," Mary said.

It was all fixed that evening. Dick and his Uncle George came to the house. George had extensive business interests in London

18

and he had just bought a London practice from the Executors of a Solicitor who had recently died. His plan was to remain in practice in the provinces and spend two or three days a week in London, but he wanted a partner to look after the London office. He offered me the job on six months' probation and if we liked each other, a full partnership at the end of that time.

As they were leaving, George fell over the crane which was still lying on the floor and I had to sit up half the night straightening out the crumpled strips and bars.

I was just getting into bed when Mary said: "Bill, you didn't ask him whether he acts for speculators."

PATTERN

I HAD OF COURSE heard that of the many roads which lead to ruin, partnership is about the surest. But I have also seen admonitory notices on our highways which read: 'Danger. Road liable to subsidence.' And the question which immediately arises is, what to do? Should one pray or repeat an incantation or wait silent and watchful until the road slowly subsides. Or drive on? And so with partners. Should one stand aside and watch the ruin compassed by evil men or should one take a chance?

George and I took a chance. As partners each of us had it in his power to ruin the other: for the fraud, neglect or default of the other, each of us was liable to the last penny of his assets, a matter which affected George very much more than me, since I was within counting reach of my last penny.

The relationship between partners is, in a sense, closer than that between husband and wife and if one had, on the law of averages, to choose one bad egg in a lifetime, it would perhaps be better all round for it to be a wife rather than a partner. There is, I know, a sufficiency of cases on record of wives ruining their husbands. But timely and judicious consultation between husbands and their solicitors can considerably diminish the scale of the ruin. And a divorce is quicker to get and usually costs less than a partnership Action. When trouble arises between partners, however, the scale of consequence tends to be cosmic: and not least because proceedings between partners take place in the Chancery Division, an area of the Court whose moving parts work so slowly that it is not only to the outsider that they appear petrified.

And so when people say to me that marriage is a partnership, I tell them how lucky we are that it isn't, and please to be careful where they talk such nonsense. There are still people simply aching to get more rights for women and society hasn't yet recovered from the impact of those they've got. And when they say how careful you have to be in choosing your partner, I remember that I exercised no care at all. I needed a partner and I grabbed the first one I could reasonably bear to have near me. And although the element of choice may seem to be greater in marriage, I doubt if it really is. In both cases one is bedevilled by need and I should have thought that the biological urge would cause more confusion than the simpler urge to earn a living.

But the successful working of both institutions, like so much else in life, depends mainly on chance. With a partner as with a spouse, you don't really know whether they're going to stand up until you live with them, day in and day out. Even then you may not know. The truth behind the person may not emerge until they face catastrophe. And then it's too late.

And if it be asked why have a partner at all, in my case I needed one because I had no money and no clients and because I am not made of the stuff of those men who can put up a plate and wait. That seemed to me too much like the spider and his web. And George wanted a partner to deal with the contentious work which he disliked. He played golf and bridge with the directors of large companies for whom he created and then managed trusts, made their wills and in due time attended their funerals. He then administered their estates. He was forever buying and selling houses for them and their families and friends and business premises for their companies. He formed new companies and wound up old companies and generally occupied himself with all the business arrangements which people make with each other.

All of which he did very well. He has a tidy mind and can build brick upon brick a highly competent legal structure. But he hated trouble, mostly I suspect because he has an ineradicable conviction that all trouble is avoidable. And when he found that he couldn't avoid it, he looked for someone else to take it on. And that was me.

Because trustees default, contracts are broken, divorce plays havoc with marriage settlements and forgotten relatives angrily contest the justest of Wills. These are untidy things and the machinery of the Courts has to be invoked. George dislikes invoking it. So he looked for a partner to do the litigation. And there is a curious by-product of this division of the work between us. At the beginning, our clients tended to be drawn from the same pool and to some extent it is still true, but even at the beginning it was sometimes hard to recognise. And as the years have passed it has become more than ever clear that, whether or not drawn from the same pool, our clients belong to two different nations. George acts for one and I for the other, and while they sit nameless and unannounced in the waiting-room, they are as identifiable as if they had been branded.

The people for whom George acts are solid respectable men of substance. They are protectors of their families and businesses, men of the Establishment. But I deal with all the trouble and so my clients tend either to be neurotic or neurotic about their trouble, which so far as I am concerned, comes to the same thing. Still George likes his work and I like mine which is fortunate for everybody, particularly our clients, because it seems to me that it just isn't possible for a normal man to be expert in all branches of the Law. So for us, partnership has resulted in a fairly good working arrangement.

At the beginning, George spent more than half the week in the provinces which was perhaps the largest factor in the success of our partnership. Doing such very different work requires differing attitudes and qualities in its practitioners and we are as people, very unalike. Had we lived closely together from the beginning we might have driven each other mad, but it was three years before George gave up the provincial practice to stay in London the whole week. And by that time, we had got used to each other and to the idea of being in partnership together. Now we each know the strength and the weakness of the other and we don't stretch the relationship beyond the limit it will bear. And as I've said, in partnerships you don't have the biological urge to contend with as well.

At first I used sometimes to go with George to his club where half a dozen large men with chunky voices discussed cricket, football, racing and the stock market with great exuberance. After some drinks came the gossip of their friends and the dirty jokes. I tried hard to be charitable. They were all of George's generation—in the fifties and at that age, I suppose drink is easier to get than women and dirty jokes a useful sublimation. But I found it oh so boring, as boring I dare say as they found me.

And yet they were all successful in their own spheres, all somehow larger than life and all with a genuine self-assurance which made it seem so very sad. "This is success", they all seemed to be saying as they bought one another more rounds of drinks, and Charles said to Walter, "Heard this one, old boy?" For the first time in my life, I realised that nothing quite fails like success and for some years after I had noticed this message lying on the rim of my mind, I didn't entirely know what I meant.

But now that we both have knowledge of each other, we frequently meet socially, although always on neutral ground. He doesn't take me to meet his sporty friends and I don't take him to meet my arty friends. George's friends bring in the work too, and not only work for George but work for me also. And when I meet them professionally, I find them charming.

Thus life inside the framework of our partnership gradually wove itself into a pattern, a pattern which felt good, comfortable, meaningful. And there were no speculators.

EARLY ONE MORNING

I DIDN'T REALISE what had happened to me until George and I had been in practice together for six years and the realisation came during the week of our anniversary. The nature of the practice had by then rather changed. George's friends continued to send us work but I now had a considerable practice of my own, a good deal of which was divorce. George disliked divorce; he thought it was messy, another trouble which was avoidable. But if he objected to the newer direction the practice was taking, he didn't say so. Sometimes I wondered why I should get so much matrimonial work but I never saw the point until Willie Vincent stuck it under my nose.

The week was like most other weeks: there was always too much to do and never enough time to do it in. But a flaming row with Mary took place at the beginning of it. It was early in the morning, which is I suppose the best time of day for a woman to start a row because she can get in what she wants and then, when the man has roused himself enough to retaliate, she gets the clock to strike and he remembers he has to go to work. And the row is over, with woman triumphant and man disgruntled, cheated and late for work.

It started in the familiar way.

"Will you be home early this evening, Bill?"

"I don't know until I've seen what's in my diary. I'll ring you later." I was slightly jangled. She'd asked this question a hundred times before and always got the same answer. At least she could occasionally re-frame it. I went into the bathroom to shave. Mary followed.

"You know," she said firmly, "the Grandisons and their children are coming for the week-end. You will be here, won't you?"

Today was Monday, not even completely Monday since I wasn't dressed yet. The week-end seemed a long, long way away. I had also quite forgotten about this arrangement.

"The Grandisons?" I said. "Was it this week-end?"

I suppose I sounded disinterested. I certainly felt disinterested. I didn't care if I never saw the Grandisons for the rest of my life. And I didn't like being cornered in the bathroom either.

"But you will be here?" she persisted, frowning.

I dissembled: "Really," I said, "it's only Monday and you're making plans for next week-end. I hate making plans, especially in the bathroom. Let's talk about it later in the week."

"Then I can rely on you," she said half anxiously. "You will be here at the week-end?"

I should have been on my guard. But it was eight o'clock and I was shaving and privately putting myself together to face the day. The world is a predatory place and nowhere more predatory than in the home. There is also no fiercer antagonist than one's wife because she has access where more obvious foes have none. Normally I knew all this but my guard was down and I bungled.

"No, don't rely on me," I said carelessly, "I may have to work at least one day of the week-end. But it depends on how much I get through during the week."

"Can't it wait?" Her voice was very quiet.

And now I knew what was coming. It had come before. I turned to her. Her face was white and she was trembling.

"Mary, you know what the job's like." I tried to be gentle and moved towards her to kiss her, but she backed away.

"Yes, I know what the job's like," she mimicked, and then came the attack spewed directly at me: "But what about us, me and the children? You spend all your time in your office. Your energy all goes in taking care of other people's troubles— all these ridiculous people who don't care twopence for you. And when I ask you to spend a little time with us, you're always too busy. You seem to think that if you give me money and pay the bills, that's all you need do. But what kind of a life do you think we have?" She stopped, very close to tears. Then she said pleadingly: "Bill, why can't you be more with us? You give so much of your time to other people, strangers, why can't you give more of it to us? Surely we have the first call on you?"

She stood waiting, her dark curly hair tumbled all over her face, and her eyes swollen. I suppose I should have felt tender, but all I felt was irritation. I tried to be reasonable, the kind of reasonable one is at eight o'clock in the morning. "Of course you have the first call on me," I said, in the friendliest voice I could find. "And of course I would like to spend more time here, but the work keeps coming in and I can't get through it all during the day because there are too many interruptions. And there are some things I can't leave any longer and if this week is like last week and the week before that, I just won't have time to do them. So that means I shall have to work on Saturday or Sunday. But," I said feeling virtuous, "I'll only do what's really urgent and that shouldn't take very long."

She stood at the door irresolute, an attitude of hers which I always found maddening, because it suggested to me that she would neither go forward nor back but would stand there, impeding me in the only way left to her. I turned back to the mirror and as I shaved the last of the lather from my face, I said:

"It is an extraordinary time to have this discussion, isn't it? Can't we talk about it this evening?"

"This evening!" she repeated. The irritation had communicated. "Have you no idea what you're like in the evening, after your clients have been feeding on you all day? They've had the best of you and all we get is the wrong side of your temper. The only chance I ever get to talk to you is at this extraordinary time." She was mocking again. Then she said: "Anyway, you're such a moody devil that it's only at this extraordinary time that I have any idea what mood you're likely to be in. At any other time of the day, I can never tell what you're going to be like."

I was tired of her telling me I was moody. Nobody else ever said it and for a moment I stopped trying to be reasonable and hit back: "Why should you expect me to be the same all the time? Nothing else is. The weather's different every day, even the streets don't look the same all the time—the light is different, the colour is different, the shapes are different. And aren't I and aren't you a reflection of all these things? Of the food we eat, the clothes we wear, the people we meet?" I paused and said slowly, "And of the love we get?"

She didn't answer. I tried again to be reasonable.

26

"Look here," I said, "I do a job, a professional job and it exacts certain conditions of me. If I weren't prepared to fulfil those conditions, I couldn't do the job properly. And that's how it is," I ended lamely and began to wash my face.

"Yes, I know," she said slyly, "and one of the conditions is that your clients' interests come before your own." She was repeating what I'd told her many times before, but she made me feel a prig. I tried to control my anger and in the attempt said more than I meant:

"Yes, that's right. You know the kind of people I see every day—people in trouble. And you can't just turn it all off at 5.30 and go home, or I can't anyway. If you're prepared to do the job, you have to accept what it involves and what it involves means that my own personal interests are subordinated. But I can't live my private life like that as well. That must be separate. That's why I'll answer the telephone at the office but not here. That's why I'll allow my arrangements at the office to be altered to meet emergencies, but I don't want any emergencies here. That's why I'm prepared to do things for my clients which I wouldn't do for myself. But when I leave my office and come to my home I stop being a solicitor and nobody, not even you, can exact those conditions from me any more. Here I live my life on my own terms."

"So if one of your clients wants you to do something you don't want to do, you do it. But if the children or I want you to do something you don't like, you won't." It was the truth and not the truth. A dozen times we'd reached this impasse. She believed what she'd said. For her it was true. I knew it was wrong. But there seemed to be no way of reaching her, of making her know it was wrong. Between what I wanted from life and what she wanted, there was a huge gulf in which conflict perpetually raged between opposing interests and needs. And communications across the gulf were sporadic, sparked by a good night in bed or a chance moment. Sometimes I wondered privately how men and women ever managed to live together at all. "No, it just isn't like that," I said finally. "But please Mary not now. Let's talk about it later."

"Just one more thing Bill," she replied. "Tell me why it is that George doesn't have to work so hard as you. George allows nothing to interfere with his golf or bridge. How is it he can manage and you can't?"

"Because we do different kinds of work, that's why. His kind of work isn't done in a hurry and mine sometimes has to be."

"The truth is of course," she said flatly, "that you prefer to be in your office. You find us boring, don't you?"

I was trying to wash my ears, but with soap in them I knew I shouldn't hear what she was saying and this was evidently not the moment to say "What?"

"You know that simply isn't true," I said comfortingly. "It's just that there's too much work." And as she opened her mouth for the rejoinder, I stopped it because I knew I was going to lose my temper if she said it.

"And we can't get another partner because the practice won't stand it," I added in the voice which I used to end an over long interview.

But she wouldn't end it:

"Then why can't Henry do some of it?"

"Henry's got enough of his own to do. And anyway he's unadmitted and you know perfectly well what clients are like. They want me to do it."

"But you've often told me that in other firms some partners leave everything to their clerks. Why can't you leave some of your work with your clerks?"

I could see this was going to lead to a full-scale battle unless it was stopped.

"I've also often told you that our practice isn't like that and my part of the practice in particular is personal to me. My clients want me to do their work myself and I have to do everything I can't pass on to somebody else." Then I said pleadingly: "Now please Mary, I must get ready."

"You just want to be better than other people," she said as she finally turned to go. I was furious. I seized her by the arms and thrust my soapy face into hers. "You listen to me once and for all, you stinking bitch. I don't want to be better than anybody else. All I want is to do the job as well as I can. And not because I win cases or to please clients. I don't care if they're pleased or not. I do it to please myself. If I do a job badly, it annoys me, not because I've lost a client but because I've damaged my own standards. I don't suppose you know what I'm talking about

28

because you haven't got any standards. But I'm sick of having battles with you. I spend all my days battling. Here I want peace, not a constant opposition. Now get me some breakfast." And I pushed her out of the door.

I looked at the clock. Gone half-past eight. I'd lost my bath. And that made me angrier than ever.

MONDAY MORNING

I WAS STILL ANGRY when I got to the office. I was also late. I was always coming in late and recently it had begun thoroughly to get on my nerves. I should have got in by half-past nine and then there was time to look at the post before the day started to run away from me. But I never did. And now that I couldn't rely on my watch any more, I was getting later and later. For years I had known that my life was twenty minutes slow and to compensate I used to keep my watch twenty minutes fast. In this way I had managed for a long time to keep up with other people, more or less, particularly in the morning when my need was greatest. But one day the trick stopped working. After that, every time I looked at my watch I automatically deducted twenty minutes. It had happened suddenly without warning. It was of course a warning in itself, but I didn't know this at the time and I'd simply transferred the trick from my watch to my secretary. It was almost as comfortable and in each case I was able to avoid the reality.

As soon as I got into my room, Anne brought Jordan in. He had been waiting for me, but a cup of coffee seemed to have kept him happy enough. Perhaps happy is too strong a word. I never saw anybody in my office who was happy but at any rate he was affable. And he wanted a divorce and it was not very straight-forward. I had read the file a few days earlier, so I knew the facts pretty well.

We had presented a petition for divorce against his wife on the ground of her cruelty. She had consulted solicitors who were defending the proceedings in the ordinary way. Last week her solicitors had written to tell me that she had just been certified as of unsound mind. Now I had to explain to Jordan how it affected the prospects of divorce.

He didn't see the point at first. "Surely," he said, "the fact that she's mad will strengthen my case. Only a mad woman would have behaved as she did."

"I'm afraid not," I replied. "To be guilty of cruelty you have

30

to intend to be cruel and if you are insane, what may appear to be a cruel act, may not be such in Law because it lacks the intent to be cruel. It has only recently become necessary in the Divorce Division to enquire into the state of mind of the spouse who is alleged to have been cruel. Previously it had been held that the Court's duty was only to the spouse who had been injured, but a recent decision in the Court of Appeal has made applicable to the Divorce Division that part of the Criminal Law which is concerned with insanity. And now the Divorce Court will enquire whether, at the relevant time, your wife knew the nature and quality of her acts and if she did, whether she knew them to be wrong."

I stopped with a jerk, on a wrong note and cursed myself for falling into the jargon again. I was anxious to avoid it with Jordan. He needed help, not clever talk. Carefully I went on:

"Let me give you an analogy. Not long ago, a man hit two of his children over the head with a hammer and killed them. When his wife came in, he tried to strangle her. He was tried at the Old Bailey and found guilty but insane. Later, his wife tried to divorce him for cruelty but the Divorce Court decided that as his insanity had prevented him from having the necessary mental intent to commit a crime, it also prevented him from having the necessary intent to commit cruelty."

Jordan leaned forward: "So she didn't get a divorce?"

The telephone rang. I picked it up.

"No calls, Joan."

"It's Mrs. Heffer," she said and put her straight through.

"Mrs. Heffer," I said shortly, "the Summons for the Injunction is on tomorrow at 10.30. Come if you like, but there's nothing you can say. All the evidence is taken on Affidavit."

Mrs. Heffer was in tears.

"I should like to come," she said.

"Very well, be here at 10 o'clock and I'll take you over."

I rang off abruptly and immediately felt sorry. Mrs. Heffer had had all her furniture put on the street four days ago by her landlord and we were applying to the Judge to get her put back into her flat. But that was tomorrow at 10.30 and now it was not quite eleven and the day to get through.

I turned back to Jordan. He was looking a bit grey. I rang the bell:

31

"Bring in some coffee, Anne."

He moistened his lips: "So she didn't get a divorce?"

"No," I said, "she didn't." Then I tried to cheer him up. "But we don't know yet whether at the time your wife committed the acts of cruelty, she was insane. She may have been sane then. The insanity could have developed later."

I don't suppose I sounded very convincing. I didn't feel very convinced. But as I looked at him, I saw that he wasn't listening. He was sitting hunched up in his chair. Then straightening, he looked me full in the face. I could feel it all coming at me, Jordan's moment of truth. I didn't want it. He was going to give me another load to carry and I had enough loads already.

"I was very frank with you," he said jerkily, "when I first came here. I told you what I've had to put up with for twelve years. I told you things I've never told a living soul. But this woman is my wife." He stopped briefly. It was an impressive moment. Then he went on: "I'm not a religious man, but I took her on for better or worse, didn't I? And if my wife is mad and didn't know what she was doing, how can I get rid of her now?" He paused and added, "Even if I could," and his face collapsed. "Anyway, I'm forty-four. I haven't got anybody else and I'm too tired to make a fresh start, even if I had." He was looking at me with the look I'd seen so often before.

I stared across the room. There greenly elegant I met Halsbury's Laws of England sitting primly in the book case. A terrible depression fell on me. What was I doing in this room at all, listening, always, listening, until the moment came when they said, "What do you think I should do Mr. Mortlock?", or "What do you advise Mr. Mortlock?" Sometimes they didn't say anything and that was worse, because then I could feel it all without even the dilution of words. And what they always meant, whatever they said, was "You make the decision Mr. Mortlock."

But I didn't want to make Jordan's decision. It wasn't my job. That was up to him and anyway I felt too tired. I wondered why I was tired at eleven o'clock in the morning. That no doubt was the row with Mary. But I had accepted this kind of responsibility before and made the decision, though I had always carefully framed alternatives and appeared to leave the final word with the other. Why not now? As I asked the question of myself, so the answer glimmered and disappeared, but I put it to one side for my private consideration, as the coffee came in. While I sipped it my resolution returned, but I would give alternatives, only alternatives.

"Mr. Jordan," I said gently, "only you can decide what obligations you owe your wife. But from what I understand, it is unlikely that she will ever recover. No one can be certain but that is how it looks. If you wish, we can instruct a psychiatrist to let us have a report so that we can have a greater measure of certainty of your wife's likelihood of ever becoming normal again. He can also give us some indication whether at the time we allege cruelty, your wife was able to form the necessary mental intent. On that report you can make your decision. If the psychiatrist finds that at the time of the cruelty, your wife was probably insane, your decision is made for you, because you won't get a divorce for cruelty. You'll have to wait five years and then you can use insanity as a ground if you wish. If he finds that she almost certainly knew what she was doing and intended to do it, knowing it was cruel, you will probably get the divorce. Then, knowing whether your wife is ever likely to recover, it will be up to you to decide what to do."

"Couldn't I drop the proceedings now?" he asked.

"Yes of course," I said. I had done it again. I hadn't given the alternatives at all. I had wanted him to go on until he'd got the report, simply because I had decided that life for him could only be better without his wife than with her. But, I told myself furiously, this was nothing to do with me. It was his affair. I was only an instrument. Keep away Mortlock I shouted inside. Mind your own damned business.

People tell me that life is full of loose ends. Mine isn't—not between my clients and me. Every end is tied and sealed.

"You don't think I should drop them, do you?" Jordan asked.

What to answer? Did my refusal of involvement so recently discovered require me to lie?

"No, if you want my opinion, I don't think you should abandon the Petition—not until you've got the report. That's the time to decide."

And still no quarter: "But you think I should try and get a divorce anyway, don't you?" This was said urgently, a reply was important, his decision could only come from me.

"Well yes, I do, if you can," I said, thinking to leave it there, but I found myself going on: "Let me put it to you, not as a lawyer but as one human being to another. If your wife is to spend her life locked up as a lunatic, to whose advantage is it for you to remain married to her?"

He was silent. It is a hard thing to start life at forty-four with not much but misery behind you. And he was an old forty-four, overweight and despite his fat, somehow shrivelled. Poor Jordan, whatever he decided or whatever the Court decided for him, he hadn't had much of a bargain. And yet once upon a time I could see him leaping out of bed in the morning, grabbing the day by the throat and shaking it to make sure he wouldn't miss a second. I could remember feeling like that myself.

Then he sat up: "All right, let's have a psychiatrist's report," he said and smiled, as if he were glad to be pleasing me. And he was, because he had opted for life and that in a solicitor's office is a gladsome thing.

I had just finished dictating, when my partner put his head round the door and neighed. This is a habit of George, his way of reconciling himself to the sad truth that he looks rather like a horse. I still had Jordan sitting in my mind and I wasn't ready for anybody else yet, so I sighed.

"Come in George."

He came in, sat down and began to collect his thoughts. I knew that he was collecting his thoughts because he was stretching each of his fingers until the knuckles cracked. In all our six years together, I had never learned either to put up with this gruesome habit or to take my eyes off those unbearably hairy fingers as relentlessly each was racked and screwed. Ten knuckles cracked and fell silent. George was ready to speak.

"You know," he remarked casually, "that I've got to go to old Benson's funeral today?"

"No, I didn't know, but you're always going to funerals. Which Benson is it?"

"Harry."

"What, queer Harry?"

"Yes." George sounded a bit stiff. He was rather careful to observe the conventions, particularly those concerned with the dead and he obviously felt that because a man had been ostentatiously homosexual during his life, was no reason for calling him

34

queer after his death. Which was true enough, but everybody had always referred to Harry as Queer Harry after he had left his wife for his boy friend. I sighed again. Sometimes I wished that George had just a little more humour. Still, he spent such a lot of his time with his nose stuffed inside deed boxes that I could see that a sense of humour mightn't be very rewarding.

"I gather," said George after he had registered his offence, "that there's a to-do in the Benson family."

"I should just think there is," I agreed and began to laugh. "The whole queer population in the Kingdom will be at the funeral. I can just imagine Sarah's face and Georgina's." I found I was beginning to laugh hysterically and cut it short. This time George wasn't offended. He was too concerned about something:

"No, I don't mean that," he replied. "I mean there's been a muddle over the Will."

"A muddle? But surely you drew the Will?" I couldn't understand this. George was always most particular about Wills.

The telephone rang. I said "No calls, Joan while I'm with Mr. Gissing."

"It's Mr. Bird," she said and put him through. I was never quite sure how Joan did this. But whatever I was doing or wherever I was, she always managed to get me to talk to the people she thought I ought to talk to. And she was always right, or almost always.

"Is that you Bill?"

"Yes it's me."

"Chirpy here."

"What is it Chirpy?"

"Bill, can you draw an Agreement for me?"

I paused. "That's really George's department, you know. Would you like to speak to George? He's here with me now."

"No," he said hurriedly. "I'd really much rather you did it Bill," and he sounded anxious.

I was suspicious. "What's the catch Chirpy?"

"There isn't a catch, Bill. It's just a simple agency agreement between my Company and a French syndicate."

I was looking through my diary. I said:

"Can you come on Thursday at twelve?"

There was an embarrassed silence at the other end.

At last a winning voice emerged from it:

"Bill, I had rather wondered whether I could have had a draft by the morning."

Now it was out. I had known him during the War and he thought I would do things for him that George wouldn't. Well he was wrong.

"Bird," I said in a cold voice. "There appears to be a widespread notion among the populace that a solicitor is simply a slot machine, and that one of his slots is always marked with the name of whatever anybody happens to want at the moment. And that you have but to pull out the slot and there you are with a Will, a Deed Poll, a Decree Absolute or an Agency Agreement. I must tell you, Bird that neither George nor I contain this faculty. We are not machines. We are artists, creators of a high order. At this moment in time, the relationship between you and your French syndicate is a tenuous sickly thread. We will make you a contract which will nourish and glorify the Entente Cordiale. But not today. Come on Thursday at twelve."

I put the receiver down. Then I picked it up again:

"Joan," I said in a hard, uncreative, business-man's voice.

"I'm sorry, Mr. Mortlock," she whispered. "I made a mistake."

I opened my mouth and closed it again. "Joan," I said weakly. "No more calls while Mr. Gissing is here."

I turned to George who was lying back in his chair with one long leg folded in an excruciating manner almost over his stomach. He was gazing at his discreetly patterned socks.

"Chirpy Bird on another good thing," I remarked. "Now George, what about the Will?"

"I drew Harry's Will all right," he said. "I did it in 1947. He had just left Hattie and gone to live with a chap called Percy something, and he told me to leave all his estate to this man. Naturally, I objected and said I thought he should make provision for the children who were then all very young, even if he didn't leave anything to Hattie. He said something about that bitch having enough money to look after everybody. I did what I was told and sent him the Will. I knew that Hattie had a fair amount of money, so I wasn't over concerned. I didn't know then she would take up with that stinking share-pusher, did I?" His tone was aggrieved. He wasn't very pleased with himself and wanted to be told it wasn't his fault. But he was twenty

36

years older than me and anyway I thought it was his fault. He should have been tougher with Harry, whom I had known well enough to know was persuadable.

So I wagged a finger at him playfully. "You know very well, George that if you'd tried harder with Harry, he'd have given way about the children and settled some money on them in 1947."

"Have it your way, then. You're a bloody Common Lawyer of course and you plan your life and other people's on the basis that everyone is a liar or a thief or a cheat or a scoundrel and that accidents always happen." He was getting red in the face.

"Now George," I said chidingly, "you know there are no accidents. I specially gave you Uncle Freud for a birthday present and you don't read him."

"Bill, I came in here to put a problem to you. May I please put it?"

He looked at his watch. Involuntarily, I looked at mine. It was 12.50, less twenty minutes.

"What are you doing for lunch?" he asked.

"Sandwiches here—I've got a Summons at one-thirty—so please put your problem."

"Hattie went off with the share-pusher, taking the three children with her. He finally got through her money about a year ago and left her. By this time Harry had divorced her. So now she had no husband, no money and three growing children. Harry gave her some money from time to time and paid the children's school fees. But they didn't make any permanent plans." He paused for a moment and went on rather shyly, I thought:

"I fancy," he said slowly, "that this was a deliberate move on Harry's part. I think he could see that life might get rather difficult as the years went on. . . ." He stopped, obviously embarrassed. So to help him out, I said: "You mean that the ageing queer has rather a thin time?"

"Something of that," he said.

"Anyway," he went on more briskly, now that the sordid sex part was over, while I began to wonder why he had dragged it in, "anyway, whatever he may have intended, he only gave Hattie money when she needed it. But a fortnight ago while he was staying with her, he fell ill. It didn't appear to be serious at first. And

37

then suddenly it did become serious, very serious. They called in a local man and Harry gave him instructions to draw up a new Will. That was last Thursday. The local solicitor promised to deliver the Will for execution on Saturday morning. Harry died on Friday night." And with an unhappy gesture, George fell silent.

"Well, what are you fussing about?" I asked.

"You mean the Inheritance Act?"

I nodded.

"Yes, I did mention that to Hattie," he replied in the manner he might have used to say he had given her a tip for the Derby, "but I thought it only had a limited application."

"So it did in 1938 when it was first enacted. But the 1952 Act has widened it a bit. And now I'm afraid that Englishmen have lost one of their traditional freedoms—the freedom to cut off wife and children without a penny, as a kind of posthumous punishment."

"I didn't know of the 1952 Act," George said humbly.

"I didn't know of it myself until the other day when I heard somebody mention it at lunch in the Law Society and when I got back here, I looked it up." Then I said half mockingly, half hopelessly, "If only I could bring myself to read all those smug periodicals which arrive here every week, or, better still, if I could bring you to read them. . . ."

George shrugged irritably. He was too worried to deal with gibes.

"Do you want me to give you a lecture on the new Act?" I asked.

"No, all I want is enough information to give Hattie after the funeral."

"Well," I said thoughtfully, "there are two girls under twenty-one and the boy of thirteen. They can all claim. Once Probate has been granted to the Executors, whoever they are. . . . I suppose you're one?"

He nodded gloomily.

"And Percy's the other?"

He nodded again.

"Oh well, you needn't see him," I said brightly. "You can send him everything by post. And once Probate's been granted, Hattie can apply on behalf of the children. But they'll have to consult another firm. We can't act for them if you're an Executor. There might be a conflict of interest. There you are," I ended. "Now you can play the family lawyer to perfection."

"But you've left Hattie out," he grumbled. "What's her position."

I was stumped for the moment.

"Oh yes, Hattie . . ." I said vaguely. I got up and looked through the Statutes and then I shook my head:

"No good, George; the Act applies to a husband or a wife and Hattie isn't a wife any more."

"That's rather tricky," he said. "She's left without a bean."

He thought for a moment. "You know, it would have been so simple for the local man to have got Harry to have signed the rough draft which he wrote down by the bed and got it witnessed by two people. It's a commonplace precaution, particularly when a chap's as ill as Harry was. I expect he's insured. It seems a pity that Hattie can't sue him for negligence. Harry had given instructions for a very large sum to be left to her." He paused and looked at me quizzically.

"I suppose there is no way for her to sue him, is there?"

I shook my head.

"No," I said. "If she has a cause of action, it could only be for negligence since I assume there's no fraud. She would have to show that this man owed her a duty of care. Of course he owed Harry a duty of care. Harry was his client. But what duty did he owe Hattie? Any more than if he'd made a Will and left out half the legacies. The cheated legatees couldn't have sued him for negligence because he owed them no duty."

I paused and thought about it some more.

"It's a curious gap in the Law, isn't it?" I said reflectively, "and in my wilder moments I've often thought what a fortune an unscrupulous solicitor could make by deliberately leaving out legacies and arranging with the residuary beneficiary to split the difference. You'd be safe if it never came out." I was grinning as I looked at George. But his face expressed horror and I was glad to see, perhaps also doubt.

"George, George," I said hastily, "it was the Devil, not me. Don't worry. Whenever the thought comes to me, I push it away."

39

"Tell me," I said to change the subject, "did Harry instruct this man about any legacies?"

"Any legacies?" he echoed. "Only about four foolscap sheets full."

"I'm afraid they're unlucky," I said, "they haven't got a hope."

He grunted and got out of the chair heavily.

"I'll leave you to your sandwiches."

"Enjoy the funeral," I said cheerily.

He sniffed and closed the door.

AFTERNOON

I PEERED UP AT the clock outside the bogus Gothic monstrosity in the Strand which houses the Royal Courts of Justice. It had just gone one-thirty and I ran up the dirty grey stone steps which led to the Bear-garden. The Bear-garden is the ante-room where Solicitors and their clerks and Barristers and their clerks wait until their Summonses are called on for hearing. As I was looking at the List of Summonses Hoggins came over. He was Counsel I had instructed in the case.

"We're ninth," he said.

"I know," I replied crossly, "another bloody long wait."

He shrugged. There was no special need for me to have taken in Counsel. The case wasn't complicated. I could have done it myself but the other side had taken in Counsel and I knew from previous unhappy experience that when I had decided to do a Summons myself, if it happened to be a little out of the ordinary as this one was, something was sure to turn up and prevent me working on it during the day. That meant I would have to sit up late the night before, getting it up. And that meant trouble with Mary. Anyway I didn't like working late any more. I thought that perhaps I was getting old.

I said to Hoggins, "What do you think of it?"

"It's a curious case, isn't it?" he replied, "but I think we're all right." With some members of the Bar, a remark of this kind meant that accidents apart, we had won. With others, incurably optimistic, it had no significance of any kind, but then I never briefed optimists. When Hoggins said it, it meant nothing, but for a different reason. He said it because he thought it would please me, and if he lost there would always be some unexpected reason he could give why we had lost. His attitude was rather Japanese I thought. For the Japanese, one aspect of truth is to tell your companion what he wishes to hear. I have always found this rather an attractive approach to living.

But I didn't brief Hoggins because of his Japanese turn of mind. He was a man of about my own age who had been called

41

about ten years and he had in that time, rather unusually built up a large practice. As soon as his practice was a bit larger, I should leave him and go elsewhere because I had a theory, which for some reason I didn't seem to apply to myself, that you could only get through a certain amount of work efficiently. The too busy junior got members of his Chambers to do some of his work for him and merely cast an eye over it when it was done. I did not regard this as very satisfactory. I liked the people I instructed to do the work themselves.

It is impossible to give reasons why a man succeeds at the Bar. I had my own views about the Bar, but some measure of Hoggins' success was due to his ability, which was considerable, his manner, which was persuasive and the fact that he always read his papers with care. Not everybody took the trouble to master the facts as he did, but of particular importance to me was that he did what he was told. A Solicitor employs Counsel and instructs him. Counsel may disagree with the instructions or the course of action which the Solicitor has proposed. He is entitled to say so and to try and persuade the Solicitor that something else ought to be done instead. But if the Solicitor insists on his instructions being carried out, Counsel must either carry them out or give up his brief. Sometimes it happens that a barrister will take the brief between his teeth and run off with it on a frolic of his own, Solicitor or no Solicitor. I found this galling because the barrister frequently knows nothing of the background, nor the reason for the particular instructions and a hasty decision by him sometimes causes quite needless trouble. This didn't happen often, but it happened. And once was enough for me. I never briefed such a man twice, however eminent he was. But Hoggins was not such a man and I briefed him constantly.

I had arrived at just after one-thirty and at ten-past three we went into the Master's room. A Master in the Queen's Bench Division is a barrister appointed as an officer of the Court to deal with applications by litigants in the course of the proceedings. This Master had in the space of an hour and a half taken eight Summonses and listened to sixteen arguments. He was obviously very tired of arguments.

"Yes," he said and blew his nose loudly into an enormous red bandana.

"Master," said Hoggins in his most suave manner, "I appear

for the Defendant and my learned friend Mr. Nobble appears for the Plaintiffs. This is my Summons."

"Affidavits," said the Master fiercely.

I handed in the original Affidavit and the other Solicitor did the same. There was silence for perhaps two minutes and I was fingering the little hole in my trouser pocket and wondering whether I should put my keys and small change in the other pocket when the Master said loudly: "Nonsense" and threw the Affidavits back at us across his desk. He took off his glasses and furiously began to blow on them. Then he wiped them with pieces of blotting paper which he tore with great violence from his pad. He had obviously wiped his glasses several times that day because his pad looked like a two-dimensional Gruyère cheese. While he was doing this, everybody looked at everybody else and wondered what the nonsense was and who was going to be held responsible for it. Hoggins coughed. "Master," he said respectfully, "I venture to say . . ." But the Master would not hear him out. His small watery eyes without their protectors, swam mistily inside his fat red face. "Don't venture, Mr. Hoggins; why should you venture? . . . the Plaintiffs have behaved disgracefully."

I felt better. It wasn't our nonsense at any rate. Nobble must have felt that he owed his Solicitor an effort, so he said:

"Master, my clients did their work and there is no reason why they shouldn't be paid. . . ."

The Master growled: "I think there's every reason Mr. Nobble, why the Plaintiffs shouldn't behave in this way—it's an abuse of the process of the Court," and he looked at Nobble balefully. "I will set this Judgment aside and order the costs thrown away to be paid by the Plaintiffs in any event," and he looked at Nobble daring him to speak. Poor Nobble! His Solicitor stood at his side. Should he make a last effort to prove that he did his best on a loser, or give up? Everybody waited. Everybody was on Nobble's side by this time, everybody except the Master but the Master was the only one who mattered.

Nobble opened his mouth. And then he closed it. And gave up.

As Hoggins was endorsing his brief, I said: "I'll send you the papers to draft the Defence in a day or so."

"Surely they'll settle, won't they?" he replied.

"You know what building claims are like."

43

"I hope they will settle," I said and I meant it. I don't much like acting for or against builders. I don't understand their technical terms. And I have finally come to the conclusion that I have the wrong kind of mind for reading specifications and looking at plans. They mean nothing at all to me. And as building cases are usually fought on matters of detail, I have spent hours and hours trying to understand it all, without enlightenment ever rewarding me.

This case had been interesting until the Judgment had been set aside. Wilson my client had asked a firm of builders, the Plaintiffs, to do some repairs to his house. They had done it shoddily and an acrimonious correspondence had begun which had ended by Wilson saying flatly that he wouldn't pay them until they'd put the bad work right.

The builders instructed their solicitors to issue a Writ and said they would serve it themselves. They then called on Wilson at his office and handed him a copy of the Writ folded inside an envelope and said, "You might like to look at this." He was furious at having his personal affairs brought into his office and he tore up the envelope without realising there was a Writ inside, flung the pieces at the builders and told them to get out. As they went, they said: "You'll be sorry you did that." And he was, because a fortnight later the Sheriff's Officer appeared at his home to sell him up.

Wilson came to see me the next day and we issued a Summons to set aside the Judgment for irregularity. The Summons had succeeded and now Wilson was able to defend the Action. He would be pleased, but for my part all it meant was that I had another building case. I groaned quietly to myself. I hoped the parties would settle. The costs of a building case were dreadfully high and in the end neither side was usually very pleased. There was always some bad work and always some work for which the builder was entitled to be paid. Ah well, I thought, this was one case which Henry would have to take over and he'd have to see it was settled.

"Have you got time for a coffee?" Hoggins asked.

I looked at my watch and shook my head: "Sorry, I'd like to, but I've got a new client coming at four and I oughtn't to keep her waiting."

Anne came in as soon as I'd closed my door.

"What's happened Anne?"

She smiled. This was an invariable routine.

"I've left the messages on your desk," she said gently. "There's nothing that can't wait till Miss Gill's gone except that Mr. Gissing wants to see you rather urgently."

No sooner spoken than George put his head round the door.

"Give me a minute Bill," he said timidly.

"No, not about the Bensons," I said firmly. "The Bensons will have to wait until tomorrow."

He handed me a letter. "Have a look at that. We can talk about it tomorrow."

I handed it back to him. "You keep it. I'll lose it here. But I'll come and see you about it tomorrow. Send her in, Anne."

She was young, pretty and pregnant. It looked like the Magistrates' Court until she opened her mouth. Then I knew it was something else. She was too middle-class.

"Mrs. Beard suggested I should come and see you," she said in rather a fluty voice.

I nodded. Mrs. Beard was the wife of one of George's friends.

She told me the story in a composed, matter-of-fact way, but while she was speaking I could feel there was something else, something she wasn't saying, perhaps didn't know how to say, didn't know was there to say. I prepared myself to wait. The moment would come. It always came. Only you had to wait.

She had been having an affair and now she was pregnant but the man wouldn't marry her. He'd promised to support the child until it was grown up, but someone had warned her that she ought to get a lawyer's advice and that's why she'd come to see me.

She told me various things about the man, how he spent his time and what kind of a person she thought he was. From what she said, he seemed to be about as introverted as you can be and still survive. He had also been married before and divorced. The divorce was quite certain because she had seen the decree absolute. And he was a good many years older than she was.

I didn't interrupt except to find out more about the man, but what I had been waiting for hadn't come. And yet I felt sure that there was something wrong with the story.

I decided to move in, head on.

"Do you love this chap?" I asked, in the matter-of-fact voice she had been using.

"I sleep with him, if that's what you mean."

"No, it's not what I mean," blunt, brutal words to force issues.

She didn't answer for a bit. I looked at her, waiting, watching also to see if tears would follow the exposure one way or the other. But she wasn't that kind of person. Finally she said "Yes," but the voice was hard, much too controlled. I changed direction.

"Well," I said professionally, "you can't sue him for breach of promise can you, because he never promised to marry you?"

She nodded.

"You're over 21?" I asked.

"Twenty-four."

"Parents alive?"

"Yes."

"Do you live at home?"

"No, my parents live in Devon."

"Do you ever go home?"

"Sometimes."

"Do you ever do anything there? I mean, do you ever make the tea or do any washing up or look after your father?"

She began to laugh. "Why do you want to know?"

"Because your father might bring an action for seduction against this chap if we could show that he'd lost your services because of the seduction. And if you lived at home making tea might be enough."

"Can't I bring an action for seduction myself?"

"No, I'm afraid you can't. This is a very old Action and the basis of it is the services rendered by a daughter to her father and the loss of those services caused by the confinement or any illness following the seduction. And the damages your father might recover would include the injury to his good name."

She began to laugh again. "No, that's no good, I'm afraid. What else is there?"

"You might have an affiliation agreement perhaps, if this man would agree, or start affiliation proceedings if he won't."

"All right," she said, "let's have an agreement."

I shook my head. "Not now."

46

"Why not?"

"Because you can't make an agreement like this about a person who doesn't exist."

"If I knew you better," she smiled, "I would invite you to put your hand on my stomach. That would prove the person existed."

This was much better. Now I could afford to expand a bit.

"I can see from here," I replied. "But if you really want an agreement, I'm afraid you'll have to wait——" I squinted at her middle, "three months I should judge."

"Four," she corrected.

"All right, come back in four months and I'll draw one for you. It won't sound very nice but it will give you what you want."

"What will it sound like?" she asked.

"I'll read you a bit, if you like," and I got up to go to the bookcase, but she shook her head.

"No," she said, "don't. I can guess."

I didn't pursue it. Affiliation agreements and agreements to compromise seduction actions read like heavy Victorian melodrama, full of threats and penalties against fallen girls. Presumably only servant-girls had to resort to such expedients in those days. Fallen girls of gentle birth would have had settlements made on them. Times had changed. All kinds of women now had bastards and nobody made settlements any more. But the precedent books all remained the same.

I went back to my chair and went back to the target. It was time and she was ready.

"Why won't he marry you?" I said looking directly at her.

She received me without shock, took the weight and let it find its level. Then:

"He says that he's had enough of marriage, that he won't be put inside a box again."

"And you think that's the real reason?"

Again she accepted the thrust and said simply: "Yes, I do."

I followed up: "And does he love you?"

After a pause, she replied again very simply:

"Yes, I think he does."

Now the assembly of the facts before the last plunge home.

"You say you think he loves you. He invited you to live with him but you refused. And he doesn't want to marry you

47

because he doesn't want to be tied down again. All that's right, isn't it?"

She nodded. Her cheeks were becoming pink. She was perhaps beginning to see.

"Tell me," I asked very casually, "do you want to marry him?"

"Oh yes," she said and she was clasping her hands tightly. "Yes, I do."

I settled back in my chair.

"Do you think," I asked quietly, "that an affiliation agreement is the right way to persuade him?"

She looked puzzled, so I started again: "Don't you see what you're trying to do? You want to make an agreement so that this fellow of yours can exchange an obligation he owes to you based on love and passion for a legal duty. And that will be a fair exchange for him, won't it? To be free of you and your claim on him, to be free of his claims on your behalf on himself—all for £2 or £3 a week. And you want to make him the offer! Don't you see?"

I didn't need an answer. Her face showed that she saw.

After a moment she said quietly: "You think I should go and live with him and have no agreement?"

"I think you should go and make him happy, make him understand that you won't lock him in a box, that with you he can feel safe. Then he might want to marry you as much as you want to marry him. But you ought to know what to do yourself and if you don't know, keep away from the lawyers. They won't help you to get married. Ask your Mum instead."

She smiled sadly: "My mother would say I should stand on my own feet and not ask any favours from a man."

I looked at her for a long moment and then I said carefully:

"No doubt your mother has distilled this wisdom from the happiness of her own life?"

She shook her head. I saw with some astonishment that her eyes were filled with tears. She'd come a long way.

After she'd gone, I turned to Anne's list of messages and did what telephoning I couldn't avoid. By the time I'd signed the post, it had gone six. I read Mrs. Heffer's file for tomorrow's Summons and a breach of contract on which an opinion was urgently wanted. There were more files lying all over my desk, an action for negligence against a Surveyor, a nullity suit, an Arbitration and other odds and ends. I could do nothing until I'd read them again and there was about two days' solid reading. And when could I read them, if not at the week-end? I pushed them aside. Not tonight anyway. I was hungry and tired and it was nearly half-past seven.

I stood up and looked around my room. I didn't like it much, though I had planned it with some care. Nothing in it matched. There was a Georgian Secretaire-bookcase, a mahogany partner's desk of no vintage, brown leather club armchairs, a small oak book case and a walnut side table. I had a water colour by Vines, a pastel by Dufere and several bad etchings. Papers, files and parcels were strewn untidily through the room.

I had a reason for doing this, or thought I had. I spent a considerable part of my time discussing and negotiating cases with other Solicitors. And although one saw the same faces often enough, there were just as often new faces. The less they knew of me as a person, the harder it would be for them to assess me and my handling of a situation, and as the struggles between Solicitors on behalf of their clients are often as gory in their own way as any battlefield, the axiom Know your Enemy has a very real application. What is victory for one party can sometimes mean ruin for the other. It was often worth taking a little trouble.

A man's room when he has had the opportunity of furnishing it himself or even where he has only added a touch here or there, reflects the man. For this reason I preferred, often to the surprise of my opponent, to go and see him, even though because I was Plaintiff or because suggestion for a settlement had come from him, I could have insisted on him coming to me. And people were usually prepared to let you go and see them if it saved them bother.

I enjoyed seeing how far I could estimate an opponent before any word had passed. The precise formal man is the easiest. The way his desk is laid out, the placing of his family photographs, the type and position of paper-knife, paper-weight, blotting-pad, ink-pots and the other paraphernalia, all give him away. They are set out according to a formula which grows more rigid with the years. And were I unsure that my opponent was this kind of man, it was easy enough to check. A sudden movement of the document I was holding and accidentally something on his desk was over. "Tcha, tcha." A careful replacement exactly measured with eye screwed up to judge, and there confirmation lay. Such a man is the best opponent of all because he is thrown off balance by an unexpected approach, an unconventional opening. I call this my Judo gambit.

I once settled a very difficult case which I had been quite certain to lose, on advantageous terms, when I had been dealing with a very tidy methodical man. It is perhaps fair to say that this man was quite extravagantly orderly. The first time I went to see him, I was shown into a room whose fittings and furniture were so monstrously functional that I felt dazed by their deadness. Nothing surely could be so lifeless, so sterile as these. Its occupant confirmed that the impress of his personality which the room had accepted, was exact. His papers were a model of what papers should be.

Our next interview was for the discovery of documents. He would disclose his clients' unprivileged documents to me and I would disclose those of my clients to him. I had had all my documents conveniently arranged and easy of access, but after my first interview with him, I went straight back to my office and broke open all my neat tidy bundles and turned them into a confused heap. I threw them into a sack and took them with me in the sack to the next interview. He was a little surprised to see me arrive with a sack but I behaved quite properly and deposited it quietly at my feet. He handed me for inspection, solemn but impeccable bundles of neatly tied-up papers. When my turn came, I said: "I can't think that my documents will be as neatly bundled as yours," and I emptied my sack over his desk. Even I was appalled at the sight. It was clear to us both that it would take a week just to put the papers in order.

There was a long silence. "I'm most awfully sorry," I said. "I can't think how this could have happened." He was still standing aghast, almost trembling with horror, but his mind was roving forward.

"This case is in the Commercial List," he said shakily, "and it will be heard in less than a month. How are we ever going to be ready in time?" He sounded as if he were nearly in tears.

"It is very unfortunate," I replied, "particularly as I shall be out of the office next week." Then I took a chance which was really a certainty.

"What do you think about an adjournment?" I suggested this because to finicky minds, adjournments are messy. I was pretty sure that except for going through my documents he was ready for trial. An adjournment, apart from the untidiness of the delay itself, would throw his time-table out, would mean that he would have to re-read all the papers about two months hence, which would be a further waste of his time. But above all, my mess on his desk was destroying him and he wanted me out of his room on any terms.

"All right," he said gritting his teeth, "let's adjourn."

But I knew he was mine. A few days later he rang me up: "Would your clients consider settling?" he said.

But the precise, formal lawyer of tradition, prudent and meticulous, slow of speech and performance, is being pushed aside by the newest mutation of the genus Solicitor, the clear-headed, quick-thinking, business executive type. This man's room tells the story by itself. It is alive, vibrating, almost humming. I always feel the ulcers starting up in me as I go into rooms like this, successful, expensive rooms, almost vulgar in their good taste. Behind the enormous desks sit well-dressed, perfectly groomed men. Sometimes it is hard to be sure whether the room is an extension of the man or the man of the room.

These men do best with their like and with them I adopt the muddle gambit. In response to every clear statement by such a man, I return answers of muddle and irrelevance. If only it can be kept up long enough, he tends to give way under the strain. Used as he is to decisive steps, firm action, clear thinking and straight talk, wodge destroys him. He sinks into a marsh of disorder and in sinking, because he is highly strung, panics. He can then be dismembered quite quickly.

But of course these ruses succeeded (when they did: mostly they were games I played in my head) only because no game works unless both sides keep the rules. And this I think applies not only to the legal game of litigation, but to all the other games in life as well.

All this didn't make me like my room any better. And I went home, by train, to the outer suburbs. As I sat in the carriage, my mind was jolted back to the bathroom scene in the morning. At first I couldn't believe it had happened only twelve hours earlier and then I remembered I had asked Mary to wait for the evening. And the palms of my hands began to sweat as I thought of it. I was too tired. I wanted to have a quiet meal and sit in a chair and listen to some music. I didn't want to fight anybody at home. I was sick of fighting. And I didn't want to talk much either. Nobody told you anything by talking. What I wanted to know, I wasn't going to discover from talk. What they told you was designed to stop you finding out anyway. Like that wretched Gill girl who had needed a man to tell her how to be a woman, because her mother had taught her to compete with men and not how to unite with a man. So she came to me for legal advice, when what she wanted to know was how to get a husband. So much for talking!

As I drew away from Miss Gill, I felt the tiredness rising in me again. This tiredness was more than just fatigue. This was no cynical Samuel Butler Notebook entry: "Life is one long process of getting tired." All my energy was sapped. And I knew it had to do with Mary, but that was all I knew, except that somehow I should have to deal with it. But how?

Again the answer which had glimmered briefly in my mind as I was talking to Jordan confronted me, but it was gone before I could reach it. And in its place I saw Mary's face as I had not seen it for a long time. We had been sitting by the fire several years earlier and I heard her saying:

"Bill, I know you spend your time trying to put other people's affairs in order, but how is it that you can't see that everybody fails somewhere and that they have to accept that failure? Yet you seem unable to live with failure yourself."

"What do you mean exactly?"

"I mean us. Of course we're not exactly right but nor is anybody else. Everybody fails everybody at one point or another. Why can't you accept that? I love you and I do my best for you, but that doesn't seem to be enough for you."

"It isn't that. It's only that when I get home tired and come into this room, and you're sitting on the newspapers and the sewing's on the floor and everywhere there's untidiness, I can't seem to stop myself lashing out at you. I don't know why I do it to you. I don't do it to anyone else and they're also messy and untidy."

"Each time we have a scene Bill, something happens to us. And sometimes I get frightened because the whole thing seems to be getting out of my control."

52

She'd had a tight drawn look on her face and I put out my hand to hers:

"Don't worry darling. It'll be all right. I shall have to learn to live with my private failure."

She'd smiled crookedly and squeezed my hand: "Bill please try, because it's very important for us all."

I got out at the station and walked to the house. We'd never had another conversation like that. It had just got worse until now we couldn't even talk. All we did was to snarl at each other.

I let myself in. There was a note on the kitchen table. "Willie Vincent rang and asked you to ring back. Mrs. Gray rang that her family are at her again and Sheila Smith wants to know about her husband. They all sound desperate—not Willie—only you can help, they say. Am going out. Your supper is in the oven. Mary."

I could see the smile on her face as she wrote the note. But I was too tired to work myself into a rage and had my supper instead. I could see her point. Both Mrs. Gray and Sheila were a bit mad, but then everybody has their own private Mrs. Grays and Sheilas to put up with, even people who aren't Solicitors. Mrs. Gray was always having trouble with her married children with whom she lived successively. There was nothing anybody could do for her, and all she really wanted was someone to whom she could pour it out. Words for her were a specific, a means by which the pressures of living could be relieved. Mary and I had used to take it in turns to listen, but Mary wouldn't do it any more. So I listened. Mostly I didn't mind. I didn't have to listen very hard.

Sheila was also a nut. I had known her years ago, before I was married, but I hadn't seen her for a long time until a few months earlier when she'd consulted me about a divorce. She said that her husband was committing adultery. When I asked for evidence, she said he consorted with prostitutes. The conversation had then gone something like this:

"Sheila, how do you know?"

"Because he told me."

"Where does he meet these prostitutes?"

"In a hairdressing saloon."

"In a hairdressing saloon?"

53

"Yes, what's so strange about that?"

"Well, it is rather strange, isn't it? How do you find prostitutes there?"

"There's a manicurists' department in the saloon and they have cubicles and they do it in the cubicles."

I thought for a moment: "And your husband told you all this?"

"Yes," she said.

"Well, why did he tell you?" I asked. It seemed a pretty extraordinary thing to tell.

"Because we had a row and I said he had other women and he said Yes, he had, and they were whores and they were better than me."

"Sheila, are you sure this is true—I mean that he has whores?" I added hastily.

She nodded.

"Did he tell you where this place is?" I asked.

"No," she replied, "he wouldn't. All I could get out of him was that he went by car on the way to his factory, that he left his car outside with the engine running so as not to arouse suspicion, and that they have young girls of seventeen and eighteen and always new ones."

I stared at her. "Are you sure he's not pulling your leg? The very thing to arouse suspicion would be to leave your engine running."

She set her lips. "I'm sure it's true," she said firmly. I would have laughed had I dared. Instead I said seriously:

"Sheila, isn't it possible to put this marriage right? Surely it's worth a try, isn't it?"

She shook her head obstinately: "Not after what he's done. No, I'm going to get evidence and divorce him." Then she said irrelevantly: "He's been to a psychiatrist you know."

"Oh," I said. "What did the psychiatrist say?"

"Well *he* says he says that it's no good unless I go too."

"That's probably right, isn't it, Sheila? The psychiatrist ought to see you both if he's going to help. Why don't you go and have a talk to him?"

Again she shook her head.

"No, no," she said impatiently, "I'm too spiritual to be psycho-analysed."

"Well," I said briskly, "how are we going to get the evidence?"

"I suppose we have to catch him red-handed?" she asked.

"I'm afraid we do, unless he'll admit his adultery. Will he?"

"No," she said gloomily, "he just laughs when I tell him I'm going to divorce him. 'Tell me how,' he says, 'just tell me how.'"

"I'd like to know that myself," I said. "I don't see that I can put an enquiry agent on to a case like this. It would cost a fortune. Anyway, where's his factory?"

It seemed there was a distance of over fourteen miles of built-up thoroughfare between their home and the factory.

"There must be hundreds of hairdressing saloons in that area, Sheila," I said finally. "How on earth are you going to track him down? We don't even know how often he goes. You might go to the right shop on a day he isn't there."

"I'll find him," she said in a determined voice, and thenceforward, twice a week she left the house half an hour before her husband and went by bus along his route, stopping at each hairdressing saloon to look for his car with its engine running. I tried to point out that he was bound to know what she was doing, but she was certain that he believed her feeble excuses. I couldn't stop her and when I saw that it was giving her some sense of purpose, I didn't try any more. Every week, solemnly I received her progress report on the telephone at home. She didn't trust my girls at the office because she thought they listened in. Every week the report was the same. Nothing.

As I was going into the sitting-room, I fell over a lamp. There were lamps all over the house. Mary had a mania about lamps. I used to think she liked light, but now I knew it wasn't the light at all. She rarely switched them on. She just liked collecting bottles and as it would probably have been embarrassing to have had hundreds of bottles cluttered about everywhere, she explained it to herself by making lamps out of them. Bottles with lampshades on are acceptable. Just bottles are not.

And everybody was always falling over them, but I'd given up arguing. Every time a bottle came into the house, I watched over it and when it was empty I threw it away before Mary noticed. But sometimes I was too late and the bottle disappeared. The next time I saw it was when I fell over a new lamp.

I disentangled myself from the flex and went into the sitting-room and lying in the chair, played a record. Then I rang

Willie Vincent, but there was no answer. So I played some more records and when I felt emptied, I went upstairs to bed. I was awakened by the front door slamming. I looked at the luminous dial of my watch. It was one o'clock less twenty minutes. When Mary got in beside me a few minutes later, I pretended to be asleep.

TUESDAY

Nᴇxᴛ ᴍᴏʀɴɪɴɢ I was beginning to shave when Mary came into the bathroom.

"I thought you'd like to know that I've put the Grandisons off for the week-end," she said.

I tried to concentrate. "Oh, why?"

"Because I couldn't face them by myself." Then she hesitated and went on in a different kind of voice. It was too early for me to identify it. At that time of day I could just recognise my own face in the mirror. But that was about all I could manage.

"I may be away myself for the week-end," she said in this voice. "I'll get Henriette to come in and look after the children."

"Where are you going?" I asked. I was concerned. She'd never done this before.

She shrugged. "Nowhere in particular."

"That's a funny place to go."

"Let's discuss it tonight, shall we?" she said, and went out.

As I looked at myself in the mirror, I wondered what I had done to turn this woman into such a bitch. Because she hadn't been a bitch and she was a bitch now, or at any rate she was a bitch to me. Something must have happened or not happened to have done this. And I had no doubt as I looked in the mirror that I was seeing the cause of it. But how? Where had I gone wrong?

I didn't know, so I thought of Henriette instead. She came from the French part of Switzerland, but she had the lank greasy black hair which so many Frenchwomen seem to have and what with her name and this hair I always thought of her as French. And I never quite got reconciled to the hair, which I vaguely resented. I always thought that women called Henriette wore their hair in a bun.

We had once employed her to help Mary keep the house tidy and look after the children. I don't know how she looked after the children, but she was, if that was possible, untidier than Mary. No drawer was ever shut, everything everywhere bulged, every door throughout the house was always open and everywhere there were lamps with trailing flex. Sometimes I thought I would go mad. I caught myself creeping round the house, shutting doors, taking out all the hanks of wool, balls of string, darning materials, buttons, patching cloth and a thousand things beside which prevented the drawers from closing. But then I had nowhere to put them except back in the drawers which continued to bulge. I think it even frightened Mary because for a few months she got a job in the mornings in order to keep out of the house. But I made her give it up because of the bacon and egg.

When Mary had her job, Henriette cooked the breakfast. She was a nice enough girl and she had a few ideas. But one of them was that the English only eat bacon and eggs in the morning. And nothing could budge her from this. I used to lie in bed thinking of all that grease, and my gorge would rise. Every morning as the reality of that slimy meal crept nearer, I could hear my Aunt Lucie's voice in my ear telling me how wicked it was to waste food, that there were millions of hungry people who would be delighted to eat bacon and eggs every day. But it was no good. I was just not one of those people.

I had asked her if she could please sometimes cook something else, but she had taken this as a deadly affront:

"Monsieur does not like the way I cook his bacon and egg?"

"Yes, yes, you cook them perfectly, but is there not something else?" And her lip would tremble. And I would apologise.

When I was in a black mood, I wouldn't eat it. Next morning she would stand over me and say half plaintively, but half something else which was perhaps not menace but not very far from it:

"Monsieur did not feel well yesterday?"

I had two alternatives. If I said I had not been well, she would begin to fuss about my health. If I said I had been in a hurry, she would give me a lecture about the importance of meals. And whichever alternative I chose she would say anxiously:

"Monsieur is not angry with me?" And I had to reassure her.

I had sometimes said to Mary, "Will you for God's sake tell that girl that I'm sick to death of bacon and eggs. Even an occasional sausage would brighten my days." She must have said something because for a week I had a sausage with my bacon and egg.

One terrible morning I had left the house at a run without

58

going into the kitchen at all. I telephoned Mary and told her to leave her job and go home at once and throw Henriette out because I wasn't returning until she'd gone. I don't know what she said, but when I got home that evening there was no Henriette. Now she lived round the corner, having married locally and she used to come in and help whenever Mary asked her. Relations between her and me were quite excellent.

I rushed to the station, hoping that I wasn't going to be late, although I knew I would be. I didn't look at my watch as the train came in. You could never be quite sure. Perhaps I would arrive in time. Anyway it was no good looking at my watch. That way of letting in magic had gone.

I arrived just after ten. Mrs. Heffer would be waiting for me. I never knew how to arrive late, even after all these years. Should I look exhausted having come straight from a file I'd been working on all night at home? Or as the old dog who'd just left a very gay party? Or brazen it out? I expect I simply looked embarrassed. I always felt it. And slunk into my room.

The telephone rang.

"Good morning, Mr. Mortlock," Joan said very cheerfully, too cheerfully. I grunted.

"Will you take your calls now or after you come back from Court?"

"No time now Joan, unless there's anything very urgent?"

"No, I think they can all wait. Have you time for coffee? Mrs. Heffer has had some."

Another dig. I said in the loftiest voice I could manage: "No thank you. I've already had some."

Anne brought in Mrs. Heffer. Anne looked clean and wholesome. I wished suddenly that I could have looked like that. She smiled and I felt better. There was after all one world I belonged in, even if I did always get to it late.

Mrs. Heffer was nervous and on our way to the Court I tried to cheer her up. She was about sixty, middle middle-class with two grown-up children. She had a benevolent attitude to living and had had what she would have called a good life. I suppose anybody might have called it a good life. Her husband had died about ten years ago and now she was rather lonely. From what she had told me I gathered that he had been a successful business-man, a hard, exacting, efficient man. She on the other hand was a

warm soft and muddle headed woman, just the sort of person you might have thought would have driven a tycoon mad. But apparently not: they had had thirty years of considerable happiness. I liked her very much.

When we arrived at the High Court, I took her straight up to the Bear-garden. I frequently get lost in the High Court. I don't know whether it's the building or me. I suspect that it is me, though this is not to pay any compliment to the building. It's rather awkward getting lost when you're escorting a client over what he thinks, with some justification, are your preserves. But even I can find my way to the Bear-garden without getting lost. And I did with Mrs. Heffer.

We walked over towards the Judge's room. It was ten thirty-five. The Judge had fourteen cases in his list and we were twelfth. All fourteen were marked for ten-thirty. I looked for Hoggins who was doing the case for me but he hadn't arrived yet.

I began to explain to Mrs. Heffer that we were going to be there all the morning and perhaps the afternoon as well when Hoggins' clerk came over: "Mr. Hoggins will be here in a moment Sir," he said. The clerk was a short broad man who wore continually a wild anxious look on his face. His head bobbed hither and thither seeking his professional clients whom he could reassure, as he had reassured me, that Mr. Hoggins would be along in a moment. Before his head lost my line of sight completely, I asked: "Is Mr. Hoggins in any more Summonses this morning?"

He answered, briefly glancing at me: "Two others Sir."

He looked like an unhappy pig which had been rooting for truffles all its days without ever finding one. Though why he should have looked like that, I couldn't imagine. He had Hoggins, the biggest truffle in the Bear-garden.

Mrs. Heffer said: "Why are we having a barrister, Mr. Mortlock? I'm sure you know much more about the case than a barrister could." She might have been right about some, but she wasn't right about Hoggins. But then Hoggins and a few of his kind were exceptions. Many are called to the Bar and if few are chosen, it isn't only luck which is the disposing factor. I have heard many barristers sympathising with each other about the harshness of the fate which rewards some and fails most. My private view was that if many failed at the Bar, they mostly

60

deserved to fail. They had over-estimated their capacity. Some of course had bad luck, some bad health, some couldn't stay the course. But by and large, the Bar got the success it deserved.

"We're having Mr. Hoggins," I said, "for several reasons. First he's a good advocate. Second he has a good manner with Judges. Third he's a good lawyer and fourth and most important, I briefed him because I think you've got more chance of winning with him than with me." And I smiled modestly.

There were other reasons which I left out, reasons which lay beyond words. One was that I was afraid. Solicitors do not normally have a right of audience before High Court Judges as barristers do, and I found it rather frightening to appear before a Judge in Chambers where he sits without robes. I was used to a Judge sitting in Court in full regalia, poised, aloof and omniscient. Then he looks as if he could be in league with dark powers. The same creature stripped of costume often becomes a bald old gentleman in a dark suit with a quiet friendly voice. I found this devastatingly nerve-racking. Another reason was more difficult to put my finger on, though it was at least as real. There are barriers between the professions, between the barrister and the solicitor, but a Judge remains a barrister all his life. And I think that a client's interests may sometimes be better served with an inexperienced barrister than a competent solicitor. There is a link between Judge and barrister, as there is not between Judge and solicitor. This is not to say that Judges are swayed by considerations other than the evidence, but Judges are human beings first and Judges second.

Hoggins came over. He had just come out of the Judge's room. He looked as if he'd licked all the cream off the milk. I introduced him to Mrs. Heffer. I could see that she was impressed. She blushed all the way down the creases in her neck. He said: "I've just done one before Band." Band was the Judge.

"Did you win?"

He nodded.

"You get on with Band, don't you?" I said.

"Well yes, I suppose I do." Then he added modestly, "But you know, he's easy enough to get on with."

"I've heard other opinions," I said, "which are a good deal less favourable. Who's in there now?"

"Hanwell is appearing for a Plaintiff."

"Hanwell!" I repeated and groaned very loudly.

Hanwell was a member of the Bar who never knew when he'd been defeated. He would go on and on and on; the more hopeless his case, the more he talked. Nor did he have an interesting voice. I once knew a Texan girl to whom I could have listened for ever while she recited the multiplication tables. But Hanwell's voice was not such a one. His was squelchy, as if it had been manufactured in a compost heap while it was working. It was a disgusting voice, the kind a slug might use when mating. I could almost hear him in front of the Judge going slush, slush, slush. I couldn't understand why any Solicitors ever briefed him, although I had heard it said that from time to time Hanwell won a case, because neither the Judge nor the Counsel and Solicitor on the other side could bear to hear his voice any longer.

Solicitors and their clients traditionally like a fighter. Some of them thought that the best fighter was the man who took every point, never gave an inch, was rude to the Judge, Counsel and everybody else in Court and when defeat was staring him in the face, started to argue his case all over again. They were wrong. Men like Hanwell so often put people's backs up that cases were fought and dragged on interminably when with a little goodwill, they might have been settled. But he was still briefed and on all sides I heard of his reputation as a fighter. It seemed to matter nothing that he almost always lost. I suppose the clients thought they'd got their money's worth. And there might even have been a certain grim satisfaction in losing with a bang. Sometimes I used to wonder why the Bench didn't conspire to have him done away with, because they suffered as no one else did.

"I don't think we'll be on before lunch," Hoggins said. "He's only on the sixth and it's twelve o'clock." His tone was complacent. He had finished one Summons and he had another besides mine, so he knew he would have to hang about most of the day anyway. I expect his other briefs were marked as I had marked mine, and I had marked him ten and two. Ten guineas for the brief and two guineas for the conference that traditionally went with the brief, whether you had it or not. So three times twelve guineas took away Hoggins' objections to hanging around the Bear-garden all day. But they didn't take away mine. I was sick of wasting time in that gloomy charnel-house. It might have been pleasanter if the building had been less depressing, if the atmosphere had been more cheerful, if there had been any civilised amenities of any kind, if there had been decent pictures on the walls, softer warmer pastel colours anywhere.

To many people, the Law Courts are a place of tragedy; they enter the Courts in a grey bleak period of their lives. People in this kind of condition need help and reassurance. But we go in for awe and majesty instead. It has always seemed very curious to me that such a kindly race as the English should have such stony institutions. I suppose people don't associate friendliness with Courts, though the Magistrate's Courts and the County Courts are frequently, surprising exceptions. They think of the Courts in relation to justice, a cold abstraction isolated from the warmth of humanity, too near to revenge, too much governed by the Lex talionis. It seems a pity.

Vingtot had once boasted to me that you can understand the English character by looking at their main-line railway stations. As every foreigner seems always to be trying to understand the English character, I had paid no attention to this pronouncement. And that was before I took him to the Law Courts. Then he said sadly: "I have to return to my previous position. I do not understand the English. That they are unimaginative and dull, I know. That they hang women I have now accepted, though I cannot understand. I have myself seen them eat porridge and so I know that is true. That they are embarrassed to talk of love between the sexes, and tell filthy stories instead, I know. But this fierce grey temple which is so frightening only to walk through . . ." and he raised his hands and shook his head.

I knew what he meant. I too had crawled beneath the leaden skies of a London winter into this dank building, up its dirty-grey stone stairs, alongside its dirty-grey stone walls and I had felt like a character from Kafka. Escaping into the Strand again, I had sometimes felt like a piece of the stone wall myself, grey all through, grimed on the outside and grained and lined within. I had occasionally thought that perhaps grey was the colour of the whole English people.

We couldn't leave the Bear-garden until we had been released. In about forty minutes the Judge would rise for lunch and it was impossible for our case to be heard before lunch. But impossible things had happened before.

63

"Hoggins," I sighed, "don't you think that something could be done about the way this place runs?"

He smiled, a gentle placid smile, a thirty-six guinea look of contentment on his face, but then he hadn't got my arrears.

"Mortlock," he answered pleasantly, "every day a dozen people must say the same thing. But what's to be done about it?"

"Very simple," I said, "just buy a coffee-pot for each Judge."

"What's that?" he asked suspiciously.

I gestured towards the crowd waiting near the door leading to the Judge's Chambers. "Look at all those people . . ."

But he interrupted. "Yes I know," he said, "but it's impossible to estimate exactly when a Summons will come on, so how can you avoid the waiting?"

He shook his head. "There are too many imponderables involved."

"Imponderables" was one of Hoggins' words. He used it whenever and wherever he could. And he used it in such a way that somehow you felt there was a direct but subtle connection between the word and him, though it was clear from a hundred yards away to anyone with eyes that there was nothing at all imponderable about Hoggins. He was just a smooth ambitious hard working young man and no more.

"You know how lists collapse," he added, "and anyway you don't normally have to hang about like this because you get released." Reflectively, he went on: "I wonder why he hasn't released us yet?"

"If you mean," I said, "that no one can tell how long each Summons will last, I agree of course. But that's exactly why the system should be altered."

"How do you mean?" he asked, shifting his feet. He wasn't very interested but I was a good client and he could hardly get away without being rude. He turned his head and looked towards the Judge's door, but no one was there who could rescue him. He turned back to me.

I was amused. My hand suddenly felt skinny, like the Ancient Mariner's. But Hoggins had more luck than the wedding guest, if luck is the right word. Pander, a very earnest middle-aged barrister joined us. Hoggins turned to him with relief. "What do you think of this, Pander? Mortlock wants to buy each Judge a coffee-pot and then make them wait for us."

Pander chewed his thick lips. This was a weighty question, meriting weighty consideration. I had had discussions with Pander before. He never seemed to have any opinions of his own. His response to every problem was to cite all the authorities throughout the ages. In order to save us an hour's harangue starting with Justinian and going on through lunch to the Medes and the Persians, I broke in on his reverie:

"Hoggins thinks," I said loudly, "that we must all hang around here in case the Judge's list collapses. Well, suppose it did? The heavens wouldn't fall, would they? The lists of all the Judges are almost always too full because they're terrified that cases might be settled, and then they'd have nothing to do. Well, why not? Why shouldn't they have nothing to do sometimes? The whole structure here and in all the Courts of the land works on the basis that what matters is the time of the Court. And yet all over the country the time is being wasted of litigants and their witnesses, Solicitors and Counsel. Every day several thousands of people in all walks of life hang about one Court or another, sometimes for days on end. And though they may all go on standing about until they get varicose veins, one being alone is excepted from this drudgery of waiting. And that is the Judge. Only his time shall not be wasted. Well, why shouldn't it? Why should the Judge be exempt from the rules which apply to everybody else? And exempt, you will observe, only in one particular —when he is carrying out his judicial function. On every other occasion, Judges also have to wait. They have to wait for their wives, for their dinner, for the lavatory, for their suits to be cleaned, for the next man on the golf-course. Why is it that when they put on their wigs, they're not allowed to wait any more?"

They were both looking a bit dazed. Hoggins started to say:

"You must see that the dignity of the Court requires the litigant to wait rather than the Court, but even . . ."

He disappeared before he could finish the sentence and I saw him vanish into the Judge's room. The next case had been called and there had been a signal which I had been too engrossed to notice. As I turned reluctantly to face Pander, a movement occurred at my side. Hoggins' junior clerk was saying:

"Your office has just telephoned our Chambers sir, to tell you that Mrs. Trenchant is waiting for you."

Fanny Trenchant! I'd forgotten I was having lunch with her. Having arrived late, I hadn't looked at my diary.

I made an elaborate apology to Pander. It was the least I could do. The great authorities unfurling in his head would have to remain furled, until he had found someone else.

I apologised to Mrs. Heffer and rushed back to the office. I arranged for Henry to take my place at the Court and then moved abruptly into another world, the world of Fanny Trenchant.

Fanny's visits were usually in the nature of social calls. Ever since I had known her, she had been in trouble of one kind or another. She had had four husbands, a bankruptcy, dozens of claims for breach of contract and a constant series of rows with the income tax authorities. She was an actress, but she worked fairly regularly. She didn't come to see me often, but when she did my office magically took on the appearance of a salon. The telephone never stopped ringing and it was always for her. I used to complain about this, but she swore that it was her maid's fault for telling people where she had gone.

She had hardly sat down when the 'phone rang. "You'd better answer it Fanny," I said sourly, "it's bound to be for you," and I passed her the instrument.

"Hello," she said in the specially sweet telephone voice she used. And then her voice stopped being sweet and sounded like gravel. I listened, fascinated. I had never heard it like this before.

"Yes," she said.

"Yes."

"Well of course," irascibly shaking her head.

"Yes."

"No, I can't."

"No, I'm sorry but I can't," firmly and finally.

"No," stonily.

"Pick me up at the theatre at eleven," commandingly.

"No, wait in the car," bullying.

"No, no, in the car. I'll come out," impatiently, angrily.

"Goodbye."

As she passed the 'phone to me she smiled so sweetly, that I could hardly believe it was the same person. She didn't tell me to whom she had been talking, but I had no doubt it had been her fourth husband, obviously on the way out.

66

"Can you bear to leave the telephone long enough to have some lunch?" I asked.

Over lunch she explained her latest mishap. As she was telling me, I looked at her admiringly. Her charmingly rounded, sparkling face was framed by a mass of black hair, but the first thing you noticed was her bosom. It was enormous but firm, ripened and poised. There was no slack in it, and it didn't look heavy. In a curious way, it seemed to have an independent life of its own and reminded me of the pilot fish which attaches itself to a shark and swims just a little way in front of it, supposedly to guide the shark to its prey. Fanny's bosom was her pilot fish. And unlike big-bosomed women who are usually over-bottomed, Fanny's bottom was very discreet.

I concentrated on what she was saying. She was in debt again and her Bank Manager wouldn't increase her overdraft. She had come to find out whether she could mortgage her reversionary interest under her Uncle's will.

"But Fanny," I said, "you know it was mortgaged some years ago."

"Yes," she agreed smiling, "but that was two years ago. I thought that perhaps we could get a bit more now."

I shook my head. "Not on the figures as I remember them. I discussed them with George. And anyway even if you could find a second Mortgagee or persuade the Reversionary Company to add a bit more, most of it would be swallowed up in costs. It simply wouldn't be worth while."

"Pity," she said. "You know," she went on seriously, "I've tried so hard to keep my head above water. I've been working in this show without a break for nine months, but I cannot keep straight. It's not my fault. I watch every penny, but I just don't know where the money goes."

She saw that I was laughing. For a moment she wasn't sure whether to play the scene out and be indignant and her face briefly puckered into a frown, but then she laughed.

"The trouble with you Bill, is that you won't take me seriously."

"No, that's the trouble with you, that you won't take yourself seriously."

But at three o'clock the show came to an end. I was beginning to wonder what had happened to Mrs. Heffer. "Do you want to walk back with me," I asked maliciously, "to pick up your calls?"

She took me at my word and the moment we were in my room, the telephone rang. Patiently I handed it over to her.

"Hello."

"Oh hello darling." This was the sweet gushing voice I knew so well.

"Yes, surely."

"But of course dearest."

"Whenever you like darling."

I have sometimes noticed that there are people who play out all the gestures of a tête-à-tête during a telephone conversation. Fanny was like this. She was wriggling in her seat and blushing and lowering her eyes and behaving as if she were resisting only to attract, further improper advances.

"Yes darling."

"I'm so sorry you can't come darling. Ring me at 4 won't you darling?"

"Goodbye angel."

She blushed as she handed me back the receiver.

"What, every hour Fanny?"

She giggled as she got up. I had taken a good deal of pleasure from the two hours and who could say they had been wasted? We should soon have another divorce in the office.

But there was barely time to enjoy the reflection, before I felt the weight of the office settling on me again, as if someone had lifted it on to my shoulders and let it rest there heavily.

For a moment I thought of scurrying back to the Court, but there wasn't time and I turned to the messages and the papers on my desk. When the telephone rang, I didn't answer it. Somehow I had to deal with the letters, the files and all the other things clamouring for attention. Then came a knock at my door. I thought it sounded vaguely peevish which meant it would be Joan, furious that I had ignored her signals. So I didn't answer. The knock was repeated and the door opened. I was a bit surprised. Joan didn't use tactics like this. She would pay me out by forgetting to put sugar in my coffee, or by putting a pin in a letter with the wrong edge jutting out so that I got pricked. But it wasn't Joan. It was Henry, with a despairing sort of look on his face.

"Could I please see you for a moment?" he begged.

Henry was my Managing Clerk. He rather despised me

because he thought I was frivolous and easy-going. Henry liked boss-types and he didn't think I was a boss-type, and he was right. He was highly respectable, wore a stiff collar, black jacket and sponge bag trousers. He had been thirty years in the Law and five of these had been with me. He was short, plump, bald, earnest and clean shaven. Unusually for Managing Clerks of his generation, he didn't drink. He also knew his job and was interested in it, but only until half-past five. Then he was gone and nothing could hold him. But he was nevertheless a very exceptional Managing Clerk. We had had trouble enough until we found him.

My only real objection to Henry was that he treated the junior clerk, Stephen, as his personal slave, but Stephen never complained and I didn't see that I could interfere, still it rankled. I was always watching for an opportunity to protect Stephen against Henry, but it never came. I think Henry took care to keep Stephen hidden away from me because sometimes I didn't see him for weeks on end.

Henry was deeply contemptuous of me. His contempt took the form of an exaggerated courtesy, a kind of grand seigneur attitude towards me which I found greatly diverting. He would never have come barging into my room unless he were upset.

I was immediately anxious and betrayed it. "We haven't lost, have we?" I could see from the look on his face that once again I had destroyed myself. Mrs. Heffer had hardly touched him. He was going to use this opportunity to do something for his own purposes and not for mine. And Mrs. Heffer was my purpose, not his.

"Oh, no," he said in his most superior voice. Why had I doubted? he implied. Had I no faith?

"There was no difficulty," he continued, "we succeeded. I knew we would win, as soon as the Judge began to encourage the other side."

"Oh good." I was pleased and relieved and I didn't care if Henry saw it. Then I began to laugh. Mr. Justice Band's encouraging tones were well known. The nearer you were to defeat, the more his voice exhorted you to still greater effort. I could see him leaning back in his polished throne giving ear to hopeful losers. But he was a very good Judge, gentle and friendly and he never lost his temper. He was greatly liked. "Did you bring Mrs. Heffer back with you?"

"No," he replied patronisingly, "she preferred not to come. She said she would telephone you."

Then his tone changed abruptly.

"I simply must talk to you about these two new divorces," he said hastily. He had taken his courtesy off for the moment because he was genuinely worried. I guessed it was because he wanted to get rid of the divorces. He disliked divorce because it was squalid. He preferred to deal with cases rather than people and in particular he wanted no reminder that the area below the belt had its own special significance. He was very like my partner George in many ways and I could never understand why he had turned to my side of the work rather than George's. He was obviously made to be a Conveyancer. But he didn't encourage personal questions and I didn't ask them. I kept as much of the divorce away from him as I could. The simpler divorce work went to Stephen under Henry's supervision. He didn't mind supervising it, because then it was academic and he only had to advise on the best course of action. What he didn't like was being involved in it. And he only got involved when I couldn't cope with it myself. But he never remained involved long. He always found some way of passing on to me the work he didn't like, which meant that all the sordid things came to me. I didn't mind much, though it was occasionally depressing. But people are people and if they're also sordid, I couldn't see much point in turning my nose up at them. Anyway it was all part of the job.

"All right Henry," I said in my easy-going, frivolous way, "you want to unload the divorces. Tell me how far you've gone with them."

Now that he'd achieved his end, Henry returned to normal. He had been standing stiffly near my chair, his face creased with anxiety. Now it fell back into its usual mould and his body relaxed. But he wouldn't sit down. He preferred to stand and dominate me.

Just as I had grown used to Henry's superior manners and genteel standards, he had presumably learned to accept my deficiencies, and we worked together fairly harmoniously, though warily, tetchily, circling each other, each constantly testing the strength of the other. And he usually won, because he was more experienced and abler than me. It gave him great pleasure to beat me. Sometimes it pleased me too, just to see the look of satisfaction on his face. But sometimes it didn't. Not that it made any difference to him. He knew I couldn't do without him. In my vainer moments, I sometimes suspected he couldn't do without me.

He tapped the files under his arm. It was the signal that I was to attend. He was about to begin. His manner was half condescending, half ingratiating, very curious to see. But he wanted at all costs to lose those files, and the question he was privately facing was how far he would have to demean himself to do it. Not more than necessary, you could see that. Divorce or no divorce, a man also had his self-respect. So he said tentatively: "It's Jones and Jones," then feeling his way, "perhaps you don't remember?"

"No, I'm afraid I don't," I replied, "there must be half a dozen Jones divorces in the office."

It was clear I had said the right thing. I didn't remember. So the advantage was his. He could present the case as he chose. He grew a little stiffer, his voice a shade more refined:

"Mr. and Mrs. Henry Jones were married in 1946. Everything was all right until about 1951, when the wife began an affair with a man called Smith, a Patrick Smith. The wife's sister was at this time a frequent visitor to the Jones' household because she had shortly before this parted from her husband. Mrs. Jones in the summer of 1951 seems to have suggested to her husband that he should live with her sister while she would live with Patrick Smith." He paused. Then he said, his voice heavy with distaste, "All in the same house." After another pause to let this enormity sink in, he went on: "The two couples, Mrs. Jones with Smith and Mr. Jones with the sister, lived together like this until the end of 1953 when Mrs. Jones left the house with Smith and set up a new establishment by themselves." He stopped and waited.

"Yes," I said reflectively, "I remember something of it now. It's a rum story. But who are we acting for Henry?"

"Our client is Mr. Jones," he replied. "He now wishes to remarry."

"What," I interrupted, "his wife's sister?"

Henry didn't mind me interrupting him. It was all grist to his mill. His turn would come.

"Oh no," he said "they no longer live together. He has chosen another partner in life."

This was too smug for me so I answered it:

"Well, I can't see the Court being very happy about this arrangement between your two Jones's that each of them should license the other to commit adultery." Then more tentatively I said, "Hasn't the adultery of each been connived at and condoned by the other?" I was pretty sure that he hadn't missed the point.

"Not exactly," he replied immediately, confidently. "I did of course explain the position to Mr. Jones but I think it's all right because Mr. Jones says that he realised how stupid he'd been by the end of 1953 and that he then asked his wife to return to him. She refused and that's why she left the house with Smith. Because she wouldn't accept her husband's genuine offer of reconciliation and preferred to live in adultery with her—with Smith."

"What you really mean," I said spitefully, "is that when Jones got sick of the sister, he asked his wife to go back to him, not so much because he wanted her, but because he didn't want the sister."

Henry stood his ground stolidly. "Mr. Jones told me that he wanted his wife back and she refused. Surely as he had sincerely repented of his own matrimonial offence and asked his wife to return, offering to forgive her offence and she refused, he has the right on his side?"

"Very likely," I replied, "if it happened like that. But I don't believe it did. Isn't it more likely that Jones got sick of his wife's sister and that Mrs. Jones didn't get sick of the other man. So when Jones said to his wife: 'Let's stop playing these games and start again,' she said: 'I'm not playing a game. I love Joe'—or whatever his name is—and that left your man in the soup. And I don't think the right is on his side at all. I should have thought it was on his wife's side—though I must say right seems a pretty funny word to use in a case like this."

Henry was used to this sort of thing. He defended himself against these attacks by a submissive tactfulness. He knew he would fight another day. "Of course," he said in his most sincere voice, "you may be right, but as I am instructed, Mr. Jones genuinely repented of his behaviour and offered to forgive his wife. And she wouldn't have it. And ever since she has been living in sin with Smith and they have two illegitimate children. I think, subject of course to your views, that Mr. Jones can present

72

a petition for divorce on the ground of his wife's adultery." And he stopped, stiffening his frame as his custom was when he rested his case. I always wanted to laugh when he did this, because he just didn't have the right shape. The impression he probably wanted to give was dignified hauteur. In fact he simply looked comical.

"You think it's all Mrs. Jones' fault, don't you Henry?" I asked casually. Henry was a man of blacks and whites. The blame always had to rest somewhere, wholly on someone.

"Well yes, I do," he admitted. "Of course I think Mr. Jones was rather stupid. But I do feel he tried to put matters right and she wouldn't."

I picked up the ivory Shou Lao which stood on my desk and looked at it. It was an 18th-century carving, probably Ch'ien Lung though the markings were K'ang Hsi. I rubbed it in my hand for a moment, enjoying the smoothness.

"Henry," I said thoughtfully. "You know I very much prefer Mrs. Jones myself. She fell in love with old Joe."

"Smith," he interjected.

"Very well, Smith. What does it matter? She fell in love with him anyway, and it seems to me right that people who love each other should live together. What I do dislike so much is your squalid little Jones man fornicating without love."

Henry was scarlet. His face was again creased with worry. He knew what was coming next.

"So," I said twirling my chair to look at him more closely, "wouldn't it be more in the interests of our client Mr. Jones for you to deal with his case rather than me?"

I had him rather neatly, I thought. He wanted me to deal with the case, but he also had to reckon with himself and his own professional attitude to the work. If he really thought that a client's interests would be better served by him than by me, he was always prepared to deal with the case, whatever it was. It had happened before.

He looked at me hard. Was I serious?

He began to say: "Well Mr. Mortlock, if you really think . . ."

But he looked so woebegone that I laughed and said:

"All right Henry, I'll deal with it."

He relaxed at once, but only for a moment. I wondered why, but of course he still had one more divorce to get rid of.

"Now Henry," I said, "you've unloaded one. What's the other?"

He had coloured again. He obviously didn't fancy discussing it. Finally, he said, "It's that nasty case of Gibbons," and stuck.

"Oh I remember," I said, "the husband who pissed all over the house."

He didn't answer. He was deeply mortified. Partners who use vulgar words to their clerks are . . . well really what are they? I felt a bit mortified myself. There was no reason for me to behave to Henry like this. He was entitled to his code whatever it was. And although what I'd just said had been quite involuntary, I was altogether too fond of privately mocking him. Irritated, I resolved to watch more closely. Carefully I went on:

"That's the chap who wet the bed and the armchairs and everything else so that the whole house stank of urine and wouldn't go and see a doctor. His wife couldn't sleep on the sodden mattress and had to sleep on the floor. And she'd put up with it for years, hadn't she Henry?"

"Yes, eight years," he said.

"Now isn't that a curious case?" I said. "I remember it very well. Here is this woman prepared to go on living with this man in circumstances of appalling and quite unnecessary squalor, looking after him and getting his meals, until one day he does something which lowers her self-esteem and off she goes without warning. Wouldn't you have thought that the degradation of that house would have broken her spirit years ago? Surely a woman of spirit would have made him go to a doctor under threat of leaving him? But she put up with it, until the day she was sitting with the woman next door in her front room— imagine how carefully she must have cleaned and sprayed it to get rid of the smell. Then the door opened and nobody came in. As both women looked at the open door, a stream of urine traced a parabola in the air and rained on the carpet. Then the door closed. Poor Mrs. Gibbons!"

But Henry didn't look sympathetic; he was disgusted by people who behaved like that and his disgust clothed him like a garment. I wanted to ask why he thought Gibbons had done it, but he clearly wasn't interested. He only wanted to get the case off his hands. So I became efficient.

"What matrimonial offence are you setting up?"

"Cruelty. Constructive desertion might have been easier," he replied, "but she won't wait three years."

"Don't blame her," I said, "but have you got a doctor's report?"

"She was in a state of nervous collapse for weeks and her doctor confirms that her health has been seriously damaged."

"Sufficiently?" I asked. Cruelty is difficult—rightly difficult to prove and a doctor's evidence is usually important.

Henry nodded. His nod signified that I should have known better than to ask. He handed me three files. "This file," he said gesturing, "is Jarvis. I have taken a statement from Miss Jarvis. I don't think she has a case but perhaps when you've read it, you will let me know. She's coming in tomorrow at twelve." He hesitated and then said slowly:

"I think it might be better if you saw her."

"Why should I see her?"

"Well," he said shifting awkwardly, "I just think it would be better if you saw her."

He meant that I should accept the obligation of telling a difficult woman that she had no case in law. I pressed him to see how far he would go. I did this remembering my promise to myself that there should be no more mocking. And I went on mocking:

"You mean she's going to be difficult?"

"No, she's all right. But I think her mother would accept what you said and she won't accept what I say."

"Her mother?" I queried. "What's her mother got to do with it?"

He shrugged. "Just about everything I should think." He was losing interest. He'd handed the files over to me. Now they were my cases. I didn't press him. It would be easier to read the Jarvis file myself than try and get information out of him in his present mood. But he did what protocol required. Formally he said:

"I hope you will agree to see her."

"You know very well I'll see her, Henry," I said in a tired voice. He had had a good afternoon. You could see that. He was as jaunty as he ever allowed himself to be. And then he nodded to me in a distant manner. The interview was over.

He almost swaggered out of the room to return to decent clean work. He was a new man. And I had three more cases.

I dictated the post to Anne and dealt with the messages. "Mr. Gissing wants to see you," she said, "and Mr. Vincent telephoned to ask if you would call in this evening."

I went into George's room. It was a room with a professional manner. The chairs were designed for ease and support, the desk, tables and bookcases were period. My room I fancied to be shabbily comfortable; his I thought of as correct.

As I lowered myself into his best chair, it seemed to me to be a room in which only a very old family deed box could really feel at home. Apart, that is, from the pictures on the walls which were sporting prints of red faced men in hunting pink engaged in various scenes with hounds and horses. I had never got used to them and they always seemed to have the sort of half affronted look that interlopers so often have when they're not quite sure if they're acceptable. Or perhaps it was my own reflection I was seeing.

"Well George," I said in my most professional voice, "you wanted to see me."

He handed me the letter he had shown me yesterday. It concerned the tax affairs of an Estate which I had passed on to George and showed that the widow would get a good deal more than we had at first thought. He knew it would please me to see the figures.

As I began to read, it occurred to me, not for the first time, how much better, more humble a man George was than me. I did what I did. I didn't ask him for anything, neither his advice nor his support. And I didn't tell him anything unless he asked. When work turned up which was in his department, I handed it over to him and took no more interest in it. I left it entirely to him.

With him it was quite different. He continued to accept responsibility, even when he'd given me the job to do. He never interfered with what I was doing but I always felt him behind me. In his own work, he invariably told me what he thought would interest me and would invite my opinion, when I suspected that he knew a hundred times better what to do himself, that it was me he was really helping. Perhaps George knew a great deal more than I thought.

I handed him back the letter. "I'm glad to have seen that George," and I got up to go.

"Wait a minute Bill," he said. "Barlow rang me yesterday and asked if we'd take on a case for one of his assistants." He was looking embarrassed.

"What is it?" I was suspicious.

"Gross indecency."

"George! You know the last time we did one of those, we agreed it should be the last. They're so sordid." As the words came out of my mouth, I remembered Henry. Sordid, well why not? I couldn't very well complain about Henry and adopt his attitude myself. Feeling rather abashed, I said in an aggrieved voice:

"Anyway, Barlow must know we don't do much criminal work. Why doesn't he go to someone who specialises in that kind of stuff?"

"I said that to him, but he wanted us to do it."

Silently I withdrew my recent high opinion of George. I was too tired to argue.

"All right George," I said slowly and turned to the door. George stepped in front of me. His face was concerned. "Bill, you know what people are like," he said persuasively. "It's no good telling them that you don't do this or that work. If they've got confidence in you, they just don't believe that you're not an expert in every branch of the Law." Then he began to laugh.

"Remember that old girl you passed over to me, Miss what's-her-name, who thought her family were twisting her and I drew up a Deed of Family Arrangement?"

And then I laughed too. "Oh yes, Miss Fielding. She was so pleased with you that she forced you to go all over the place. The inquest on her cousin at Plymouth, a parking offence in Liverpool and to witness her will when she was ill in Norway. All right George, you win. When's the hearing?"

"He's remanded till Thursday. Can you see him tomorrow?"

"I expect so. I'll get Anne to give him an appointment." Again I turned to go. "There's nothing else is there?" I asked.

"I'll do your appointments for you on Thursday if it'll help. Anything special?"

"That's kind, George. But it may not be necessary. I'll see what there is."

"I'll see Bird for you if you like. He's coming on Thursday, isn't he?"

I was a bit touched by this. George disliked Bird very much and anyway he had enough of his own work without taking on mine. "I think I can probably manage," I said diffidently. "I don't want to make it difficult for you." My diffidence turned a commonplace kindness into an embarrassing situation. George resolved it. He looked out of the window and said drily:

"You're not making it difficult for me. And I have got Wilkins to help. I only suggested it because you're looking peaky and tired. I can't afford to have you ill, that's all."

So I was looking peaky and tired was I? I had thought I was looking pretty normal. And then came the voice from the window: "You're all right Bill aren't you?"

"I'm all right," I said.

I went back to my room and signed the post. Then I leaned back in my chair and closed my eyes. I was dining with Susan at eight, but I still had hours of work to do. I was wondering whether I could cadge a bath from Simpson who had a flat nearby when Anne came in, to say good night I thought. But she closed the door quietly and put the secret look on her face and I knew that something unexpected had happened. "Mr. Diggins is here," she said.

I groaned. It was ten-past six and I felt drained. But I tried never to turn anybody away if I could help it. I thought I knew what it felt like to be turned away. Still it was too bad of him to come at this hour without an appointment.

"All right Anne, send him in."

"Then I'll say good night, Mr. Mortlock."

"Good night Anne."

Diggins filled the doorway. He was over six feet tall and about three feet wide. He had jet black hair, an enormously long thin face and light blue-grey, mad eyes. Despite his rimless glasses and decent vowels, you couldn't possibly have mistaken him for anything but an Australian. He seemed to me the kind of person who would use a sledge-hammer to crack a nut, not because he hadn't got a nutcracker, but because it would never have occurred to him that a nut needs different treatment from a lump of concrete. He was the only man I had ever seen who gave me an idea of what Pithecanthropus must have been like. Not that Pithecanthropus was as big as Diggins, but the power, the sheer strength of the man was so overwhelming, was so much more and so much less than human, that in

78

seeking comparison the mind was driven back to before the beginning. When I looked at Diggins I used to feel quite weak at the knees.

But like the rest of mankind, he too had trouble with his wife. He had first been to see me about a year earlier. He had married an English girl during the War when he had been stationed here. The girl came from Sussex and from what he had told me, she had seemed a gentle, sheltered girl with thin wispy roots in life which a deal of tramping would break. How she had come to marry him I couldn't begin to understand, not that that was unusual. When I looked at my own life as a case history, I couldn't understand why my wife had married me. Sometimes I used to think of the Diggins in their great big farmhouse in Victoria, the sledge-hammer and the peanut. And as I thought of them together, I could almost feel him squeezing the life out of her, probably in quite a friendly way too, simply because the pressures he exerted on normal people were too great for them to bear—rather as if the pressure of the air to which she had grown accustomed all her life had, in the constant presence of Diggins, suddenly doubled, perhaps trebled. And she'd have to have been a Yogi to have dealt with that. But there I was, on the wrong side again. I was acting for him, and all this was only speculation.

After the War he had gone back to Australia and she had gone with him. They had lived on his farm for nine years and had three children. While he had been away on a business trip, she had run off with an English commercial traveller, taking their children with her. Nobody quite knew how she had met her lover nor what an English commercial traveller had been doing so far from his beat, but he had brought them all to England and she had taken the children to her family in Sussex. The commercial traveller had then disappeared quite quickly and Mrs. Diggins appeared now to be living a blameless, if boring existence.

Diggins had roared at her for months by letter and cable across the oceans and so much had he roared that she must have feared that one day he would arrive in his seven league boots and snatch the children. So she'd applied to the Court and got an Order for what amounted to custody of the children and making them wards of Court. This meant that Diggins couldn't take the children out of the country without the Court's permission.

When he had first come to see me he'd said that he wanted his children back. From the fierce way he'd talked and his whole appearance, I couldn't get rid of the fancy that he only wanted them back to devour them. All my childhood nightmares crept round my head at that first interview. He was the Giant of Jack's beanstalk; the Scissor man in Struwwel Peter, Bluebeard, Polyphemus the one-eyed Cyclops, the wicked ogre of all my fairy tale books. I remember having had quite a job to sit quietly at my desk without shrieking.

I had tried to be rational. I had told him that to get his children back, he would have to get the Order for Custody varied in his favour and that the Wardship of the Court would have to be removed. To do this, he would have to show pretty good reasons why the children, being as young as they were, shouldn't remain in England with their mother. For one thing he would have to explain why he hadn't defended the original proceedings to make the children Wards. He mumbled something about not understanding the papers which had arrived. Then I said I didn't think the Court would remove very young children from their mother unless we could show that it was to the children's advantage to leave her. The commercial traveller had gone, the children probably understood nothing of their mother's intimacy with him and if Mrs. Diggins could show the Court that her refusal to return to her husband was not simply capricious, I said I couldn't see any Court giving the children to him.

He had begun to foam. "But they're my children," he roared. "Good Aussies, children of an Aussie father. What right has your Court to interfere with Aussie children?" I think I must have turned pale. Perhaps he would eat me too, on his way to the children. But I did what I could.

"It doesn't matter," I had quavered, "if your children are Hottentots. To the Courts of this country, a child is a child. Their first concern is not the nationality of the child, but the welfare of the child. And the Courts here act if the child is within the jurisdiction and your children are within the jurisdiction."

"Well," he had jerked, and his chin had projected so far from his face that I'd moved my chair back, "so I have to prove that it's to their advantage to leave that bitch. And how do I do that? Isn't it enough that she's been sleeping with this bastard, that she's deserted me?"

"No," I had said bravely, "I don't think it is in the circumstances. The adultery is over and I doubt if you could prove that it's harmed the children. She would almost certainly be able to give reasons why she left you which the Court would accept. You've got to remember that other things being equal, the Court would much prefer to let her keep the children while they're so young and you'll have to have a pretty good case against your wife, before you can get over that." I gave up. I hadn't answered his question. I didn't want to answer his question.

But he pressed me. He raised his hand. I watched, fearfully; it looked like a club. It was the kind of hand you bowed to, but did not shake. He was about to hammer it on my desk. The desk would have moved away if it could. Then Diggins changed his mind and the hand was lowered. "Well, how do I get over that?" he said.

I had been forced to answer. He was my client and I had to advise him, but I hated to do it. I had said slowly and reluctantly:

"I've already told you that you'll have to prove that it will be to the children's advantage to leave their mother, and that means you'll have to produce evidence of her unfitness to look after them because of her way of life, her temperament or anything else which indicates unfitness."

His brow had puckered until it looked like a moon crater.

"She's tried to commit suicide, you know. She's tried twice."

I could believe it. I felt even less like doing anything for him. And he went on: "I suppose you mean I must start slinging mud at her."

I didn't answer. He said: "I'm flying home tomorrow. I'll send you some stuff about my wife and you can let me know."

"You're going to find this rather expensive," I had said, "if you keep flying backwards and forwards. Why don't you instruct an Australian lawyer?"

He had looked at me sharply. "Don't I have to take proceedings here to get the children?"

"Yes."

"Then what's the good of a lawyer over there?" He was no fool, whatever else he was, because he went on: "Don't you want to act for me?"

I was silent for a moment. In England, if a man wishes to consult a member of the Bar on a matter within that barrister's ordinary practice and can pay his fees, he must act so long as he is not asked to do anything improper. The position of Solicitors is rather different. There may be a number of reasons why a Solicitor would not want to act in a particular case and he is then not bound to act. But I had normally regarded myself as bound to act for anyone who instructed me, unless there were good reason to refuse the instructions. And not liking a man was not a good reason.

I could conceive nothing worse than for someone to be in trouble and find that no lawyer would act for him. It had happened elsewhere. Diggins had been recommended to me by an Australian friend. For all I was aware, he knew nobody else in England whom he was prepared to trust. And if he offered me his confidence, what business had I to reject it? It was easy enough to act for people one liked, to do work that was congenial, but it was also part of the job to do nasty work, to act for people one disliked and to do the best one could for them. Personal feelings were for one's private life, not one's professional life. So I'd said, though not without a struggle:

"Of course I'll act for you, if you wish it."

A month later he wrote to me with a detailed history of his wife's deficiencies. I sent instructions to Counsel for an Opinion how far Diggins was likely to succeed in getting the care and control of the children, and whether it was possible that the Court might let him take them to Australia.

I drew the instructions with particular care. I wanted to make sure that no hint of my own views about Mr. and Mrs. Diggins crept in—only the facts as I had got them from Diggins and for advice on those facts. Counsel's Opinion had not been very hopeful. I sent a copy to Diggins and wrote a few sympathetic lines.

I really didn't know how to deal with Diggins. I didn't in the least understand him, any more than I would have understood a mountain. This made it very difficult to advise him because I didn't know what he really wanted. I knew what he said he wanted, but I had found by experience that in matrimonial affairs at any rate, the two things weren't the same. If I could have known how his inner mechanism operated inside that vast superstructure, I might perhaps have been able to suggest an approach which might have had significance for him. But I just didn't know. And I fancied I knew how his wife worked, because

82

she was a more ordinary knowable person. Which made it more difficult still.

His next letter to me some weeks later hardly mentioned the children. It was a bitter sustained attack upon his wife. He said that he had written her a friendly letter offering to maintain her and the children to which she had made no reply. He had written again and her response, he said, had been an abusive refusal to go back to him. She had also rudely told him that she didn't want his money. His letter somehow didn't sound right. He didn't say that he had asked her to go back to him, but he had referred to her stated refusal. Nor did she sound to me like an abusive letter writer. His final words were: "What can you expect from an adulteress who has destroyed her husband's honour?"

Over the days which followed, this last phrase kept popping into my head. It seemed odd for a man like Diggins to refer to his honour. But then perhaps it wasn't, because what kind of a man was Diggins?

Then there arrived from Australia a sizeable parcel. It came by air and must have cost him pounds. It contained copies of all the letters he had written to his wife since she'd left him and her letters to him. This threw further light on the man. People who write under emotional stress normally don't make copies, unless they've had advice. I spent a whole day reading them. His letters were interminable pages of accusation and threats, typed in single spacing. And to all his abuse, his wife had patiently replied in a matter-of-fact style which was heartbreaking to read.

After this, nothing had happened for months. Until this evening. And he'd arrived without an appointment.

He didn't offer to shake hands, but then I had backed away. I had shaken hands with him once before.

"I've just come from the Airport," he said by way of apology. "I sent you a cable from Cairo to say I was coming." I nodded. There was no point in a denial. He probably had sent a cable and arrived before it had been delivered. He didn't appear to have changed. But I was tired and I'd had enough of being a Solicitor for the day. And so for the first time in our relationship, I took over the control. It never even occurred to me that he might eat me. I don't suppose I should have cared much if he had. I was snappy.

"What have you come for?"

He was surprised: "I've decided to divorce my wife," he said defensively. And as he spoke, I knew I had him. What he'd said was a lie or a half-truth, it didn't matter which. He hadn't decided anything of the kind. If he had he wouldn't have chased half-way round the world to see me and then forgotten to tell me he was coming until he was almost here. Nor would he have rushed straight from the Airport to my office after a journey like that. No, I thought, he would have sat himself down comfortably in his farmhouse and written to his Australian solicitors to take proceedings for divorce in Australia. That was the country of domicile and that was the place to present the petition. Diggins knew that. I had told him in so many words the last time I'd seen him.

So it was something else he'd come for. And it wasn't very hard to guess what it was. He wanted to get his wife back. And he'd come to me to help him get her back. I didn't flatter myself that it was me, specifically, personally me, he'd come to; he'd turned to the person who happened to know the background and whom he trusted because once somebody had told him to. And that was me. It could just as easily have been someone else. I wished it were.

I knew enough about him now, in the three or four minutes since he'd arrived, to know that if I were to control this situation, I had to lead the attack, to dominate. Because he was invariably, by temperament and natural endowment, the attacker, to get him to disclose his hand, I should have to throw him off balance, force him to the ground and let his belly rumble. Then we would both know what it was he wanted. I knew now quite certainly that if I let him make the running, he would instruct me to sue for divorce and I would have to instruct Australian agents to start proceedings. And once started, like so many other things, their own momentum would keep them going, until the decree was pronounced. And yet divorce was the very last thing he wanted.

I was always coming up against this kind of thing. People said they wanted a divorce, but what they really wanted was to re-create the past with all the nastiness expunged. If wives could be cleansed of the adultery and then said they were sorry nicely, the husbands would take them back. Mostly it was husbands who insisted on a magical purification. Wives were generally prepared to accept a symbolic rite. But if the husbands couldn't get the women back clean, they said they didn't want them back at all, and sued for divorce. Perhaps they thought by being divorced, they would be free. They soon learned that in the place where it mattered they were just as much married as before.

Of course none of them said this. They just said stonily that they wanted a divorce. Sometimes, if I thought it would do any good, I tried to expose to them this instinct for self-destruction, to induce them to stop before it was too late. Sometimes they did. But mostly they didn't. The hurt was too grave; the pride too involved. It wasn't very hard to recognise who was bent on self-immolation. It's easy enough to identify one's own.

So I turned on Diggins and said harshly: "You don't want to divorce your wife, do you? You want her back."

There isn't any word to describe the expression on his face. How could he have expected me to know what was going on inside his belly? How could he have known that I had the same kind of belly myself, only smaller?

He made only one protest in a small, rather stupid voice:

"Yes I do. I do want to divorce her," but he gulped as he said it.

"Look," I said menacingly and I felt menacing, "stop talking poppycock to me. I know you don't want to divorce your wife. You want her back. But what sticks in your gullet is that she cleared out and then got into bed with another man. You think it's her fault, so you want her to say she's sorry. She's committed the offence and you've got clean hands. So why should you have to go crawling to her when it's all her fault? That's what you think, isn't it?"

He looked hunched up and withdrawn. But he didn't say anything. I pressed him brutally, just as once he had pressed me. "That's it, isn't it? You want her back, but only if she says she's sorry. But you want her back, don't you? You want her back badly." I looked at him. He sat locked up inside himself, while I waited. I went on more evenly:

"Well you'd better make up your mind what it is you want. Do you want to be in the right or do you want your wife back? Those are the alternatives and you can't have them both."

I thought for a moment that he was going to protest again and say it wasn't his fault, but I forestalled him.

"Look here," I said roughly, "women don't run away with commercial travellers taking their three babies for no reason. And you must be the reason: or a large part of the reason. But if you go to the Court for a divorce, you'll get it all right and your wife will be found to be the guilty party. That's because the Law's got a funny language of its own. Somebody's got to be to blame before the Court will act. My personal view, for what it's worth, is that it's your fault. If your wife left you, she was driven away. And only you could have done that. And just think, she must have been pretty desperate to have faced that journey with three young children. I doubt if she was in love with the man she went with or she wouldn't now be living with her parents. So she must have faced the journey just to get away from you. And you want her to say she's sorry!" "But of course," I added quietly, "the Court won't take my view unless she defends which I should think is unlikely. The Court will grant you a divorce and you will be right and she will be wrong. It will all be marked down as a matter of public record that you were innocent and she was guilty."

He was blinking at me, wondering what was coming next. I thrust my face at him: "And what good will that do you? To have your innocence, her guilt, pronounced by the Court, you pay a price. That price is divorce. And it is too high, isn't it?"

Now we both knew where we were. He made no further attempt to pretend anything. I caught myself thinking that this was how all human relationships should be. And then I thought of my own life and hurriedly took the thought back. Diggins said in a slow exhausted voice. "But what else can I do? I've written to her again and again and I went to see her the last time I was here, but she's quite firm. She says she won't come back. I don't know what else to say to her. She's got a job and she seems quite happy as she is. I don't think she wants to come back at all." He looked as miserable as it is possible to look.

"I've seen your letters," I said. "All they do is tell her what a bitch she is. I've no doubt when you've seen her that you've told her again what a bitch she is. You've shouted and bellowed at her and thrown her adultery in her face. How do you expect a human being to behave if you do that? To offer to go back to a lifetime of constant humiliation? Of course she thinks she's better off now. At least she's got some peace."

86

I looked at him. He hadn't seen yet. It had to be made plainer still. So I went on: "Go and see her. But first send her some flowers, some gifts for the children and write a pleasant note and say that while you're over here, you'd like to see them. And when you see her tell her you love her, that life is no life without her and that it is your fault and not hers. Tell her that you will never as long as you live refer to the past, that your only concern is with the future, your future together with your children. And tell her that you didn't know how empty and useless it all is without her. Tell her that now you know. Tell her that now you will spend your life to make her happy because now you know. Make her feel she is the finest, purest, most lovable woman there ever was. And don't forget, tell her it is you who were wrong. And get on your knees and weep. You've wept enough inside. Break down and weep so that she can see."

"But I can't cry," he said plaintively. "I can't cry."

The last brutal thrust: "You're crying now. You've been crying for a long time. You're like me, like everybody else, only you've grown a thicker protective covering. Well rip it off and expose yourself. You've nothing to lose. She can't drive any more knives into you than you've driven into yourself. And now go away. I'm worn out."

As I opened the front door for him, he half sniggered as he said: "That's the queerest advice I ever got in my life."

"It's not legal advice," I replied, "but then you never wanted a solicitor. You wanted a priest or a psychiatrist. And my fees are lower. You don't have to commit your soul or lie on a couch for three years. Goodbye."

When I got back to my chair, I began to feel appalled. I was certain I was right, but it wasn't my job to give advice like that. But then what was my job? Was my duty solely to do what I was told, even when I believed that a person really wanted something else? Surely I was entitled to tell him what I could see lying beneath his words? I conceded the point to myself. I was entitled all right. I had merely gone too far. That was all. It was being tired, I thought. I should have to watch that I didn't get as tired as that again.

I went and sat in Diggins' chair for a moment; it was more comfortable. I closed my eyes and then it hit me like a bomb. Talking to Diggins was I? I was talking to myself. What Diggins had done to his wife, hadn't I done to mine? When did I break down and weep and say I couldn't live without her? When did I say it was all my fault and that I loved her beyond everything else? Diggins couldn't have been more hostile, more uncommunicative than I had been. And Diggins' life had been no colder, no emptier than mine. The only difference was that Mary hadn't yet run away with a commercial traveller. And perhaps there was just a chance that I could stop her.

I got up. I was going home to my wife to make her see that I loved her with all my life.

I rang Susan and abruptly cried off our dinner. I didn't care if she was hurt.

And then I turned out the light and went home. It was just gone half-past seven.

EVENING

In the train I began to be afraid. How was I to begin? You can't walk into a house and say to a woman who isn't expecting you, particularly to a woman who has learned not to expect you, that you love her desperately and can no longer live without her love. Perhaps you could but I couldn't see myself doing it. Communication on any level that mattered had been broken off between Mary and me and I couldn't see how to begin to re-establish it. To keep down the panic, now not far off, I manoeuvred my mind away. Why had I suddenly got this idea of sweeping Mary off her feet? And I remembered that the impulse had swamped me as I'd sat in Diggins' chair. I remembered the feeling of that chair. It had still been warm and I had felt the curious discomfort one always feels when sitting in a stranger's body heat. But why should the lingering warmth of Diggins' body have induced me to take a course of action which had never before entered my head?

And then I began to laugh until I could hardly stop. A fat old man sitting opposite in the tube looked at me sharply and the sudden movement of his head jerked a fine powder of dandruff upon his lapels, already heavily spotted. I laughed because Barbey d'Aurevilly's story of M. de Ravila's greatest love had come into my head. Ravila's mistress, the Marquise, had had a daughter of thirteen, her only child, a shy religious girl. One day the girl had confessed to the priest that she was pregnant. Under the Marquise's frantic cross-examination, the girl named Ravila as her seducer. After a great to-do she eventually explained how the seduction had come about. Ravila had one evening sat for a long time in an armchair by the fire. When he went out of the room, the girl had gone to sit in his chair and suddenly she felt a great warmth and a fierce pain had stabbed right through her body. She said she knew that this pain was a baby.

I didn't stop laughing until I got out at my station. The Marquise's daughter and I both pregnant because we'd sat in somebody else's chair.

It was fifteen years since I had read Barbey. How odd, I thought, that a fragment lodged in my memory all those years should have been enough to have changed my mood at what might perhaps be a critical moment in my life. If I were now able to catch Mary in my arms, it would be Barbey's doing, not mine. I wondered if I should ever be able to tell her.

I was still feeling pretty good when I let myself in. Mary was sitting in the kitchen eating, a book propped up in front of her. I was very cheerful.

"Hello," I said, "I got away earlier than I thought." I didn't attempt to kiss her. Now she always turned her face away when I tried and I couldn't risk any false moves. I didn't know how long Barbey would keep me going.

"Hello," she said coolly. "I didn't expect you. There isn't anything cooked, I'm afraid. Would you like an omelette?"

"Don't bother. I'll make myself a sandwich. Would you like some coffee?"

"Please."

I made a sandwich and stewed some coffee in the percolator. She looked up briefly. "Frank telephoned," she said.

"Oh, what did he want?"

"Nothing in particular. He thought there was going to be a war, but that was about all."

I grunted. Frank always thought there was going to be a war. His life wasn't a very happy one but he preferred to put it down to international tension.

She went on reading.

"Good book?" I asked.

"I like it."

"Who's it by?"

"It's one of Joyce Carey's, but you wouldn't like it. It's a woman's book."

And there the conversation died.

I walked round the kitchen with my hands in my pockets, concentrating as hard as I could on Diggins. Surely it would be easier for me. I knew what to do. I'd told him. I only had to be tender, and tell her that I loved her.

But I didn't feel very tender. Suddenly my mind was blank, a hurting, blurred emptiness. I felt wrung out, used up. And

Barbey had gone. I was all by myself and I didn't see how I was going to manage.

"Sit down Bill," she said calmly, "you're making me nervous."

"I feel nervous myself," I said as I stopped and stood on the fender.

She looked up. "What are you nervous about?"

This was the moment. I called silently on Diggins and opened my mouth. But nothing happened.

"Well," she repeated with a half smile, "what are you nervous about?"

If she had been soft and warm, if I hadn't felt the barrier between us, if I hadn't felt her control—anything might have happened. But I felt them.

"I don't really know," I said vaguely.

And the conversation died again.

She went back to her book and I went on prowling round the kitchen.

At last she lost patience: "For goodness sake Bill, sit down."

"I'm sorry," I said. "I really can't sit down at the moment."

"Why not?"

"Because I'm worried."

"Oh well what is it? Is it a case or something?" she asked irritably.

That did it. My God, would a case bring me home to prowl in my own kitchen!

"No, of course not," I said loudly. "I'm worried about you, about us."

She was amused: "Bit late, isn't it?" she said.

"Yes it is late," I replied quietly. "That's why I was worried, before it became too late."

She gave me a direct look: "What do you think we can do about it now?" she asked.

"Try and put it right—make it like it used to be."

She shook her head. "We're different people now. You're different and I'm different. We're quite separate, too. Anyway you can't put the clock back."

She seemed to be remarkably self-possessed, almost casual. A great lump came into my throat. She didn't seem to care about our marriage at all.

"Don't you care any more?" I asked, the self-pity clogging my voice.

"Care?" she repeated. "Care for what?"

"For our marriage," I shouted. "Doesn't it mean anything to you any more?"

She pushed back her chair and turned to me.

"What's the good of me caring Bill? You stopped caring years ago. It's not enough for one to care. That doesn't make a marriage." Simply spoken, matter-of-fact words, unbearably hurtful to me, true or false. I thrust at her.

"So you don't care?"

She smiled. "Don't make points Bill."

"You don't care, do you?" I repeated angrily.

"You must have an answer, mustn't you? That's one thing that hasn't changed about you. You think there must always be an answer to a question, always a solution to a problem. Well to please you, all right I don't care."

I clutched at my last straw: "But Mary," I said quaveringly, "what kind of a life is it for you without love?"

She smiled again. It was the most bitter smile I had ever seen on her face. Then I knew something of what she had had to do to stop caring. I wanted to make up for that. That much at least I owed her.

"Mary, couldn't we try and make a fresh start? I know it could be made all right, if we both wanted it to be." I fumbled in vain for better, bolder promises, for the sparkling words I had presented to Diggins. She turned her head towards me, her face pale, her lips set. I hadn't noticed until then how thin her mouth had become.

"Bill," she said in an even controlled voice, "I used to think that it was just that I was no good to you. But now I know that you're no good to me either. Our life together is just something you manage to squeeze in between cases." She shrugged. "I'm afraid we just don't fit."

"But Mary we used to. Why can't we again?"

"Because we want different things, that's why. You're no good to me as a lawyer. I doubt if ultimately you're any good to yourself as a lawyer. I know you're good at your job and that you enjoy it. I don't know that you'd be any better off merely being my husband." She paused. "I want to live privately, quietly, unencumbered by the world's victims. And you're only interested in the world's victims. You want to win cases and meet people and go to parties and argue on one side today and the other side tomorrow." Then she added thoughtfully : "It's no wonder people don't trust lawyers."

I was appalled by this. "That simply isn't true, Mary," I objected.

"What's not true?" she said sharply.

The words stuck in my throat. What was the use? I could see from her face, could hear from her voice, that she believed everything she'd said. I could feel the deadness in her and it all began to seem quite hopeless.

"What's not true?" she repeated.

I pulled myself together and returned to the struggle.

"All these things you level against me," I said hotly. "If I want to win cases, that's because I want to do the job properly. If I didn't, none of us would eat. And why shouldn't I go to parties if I want? Why must your displeasure always hang over the house simply because I like meeting people?"

"Very good with words, aren't you?" she jeered. "That's another trick the lawyers have taught you."

"That's a beastly unfair thing to say." I was angry and frightened and helpless. What was I to do? How was it that I could spend my days coping with the complications of other people's lives and yet fail so miserably with my own? My mind was running backwards and forwards like a terrified mouse.

"Unfair?" she echoed harshly. "Unfair?" She waited until the sound of her voice had died away. "Why should you expect me to be fair?" Again a glimpse of her private battleground on which she had defeated the part of her which had wanted to, been impelled to care. My stomach was turning over. My own anguish and the realisation of hers now past was more than I could manage. I was in such a state that I knew I shouldn't sleep, and I had to work tomorrow.

I caught myself in the thought and contempt ran through me. Now I would be trying to put matters right, not at all for their own sake or for Mary's sake, but only so that I should sleep tonight and work tomorrow. But this was not the time for raillery, not even at myself.

"Would you like some coffee?" I asked, my voice shaking, and got up before she could answer. We used to have very good coffee but we kept breaking the glass parts. Now we used a percolator and drank a stewed muddy brown liquid and every time we drank it we complained. But tonight it wouldn't matter what we drank.

And then the telephone rang. Mary looked at me. I never answered the 'phone at home if I could help it. I had enough of it during the day. I would have preferred to have taken the call myself this time because I didn't want to be under any obligation to her, but I wasn't sure how my voice would sound. So I nodded and she got up and went out of the room.

She was back in a moment: "It's Willie Vincent. He says he's been waiting for you."

"All right, please tell him I'm leaving now."

"I told him that," she said.

We drank the coffee in silence, Mary wrapped in her strength, and I wondering what to say next.

At last, I stood up. "I'll go and see Willie," I said. But I waited. Everything had gone wrong. It would have been better if I'd kept quiet. Yet surely something could be salvaged, even now. Again Diggins came into my head. I had told him to admit his fault and take the blame.

"Of course," I said, "I see very clearly how much I have been to blame." The words were wrong. They sounded formal, meaningless. I knew it as soon as they were out of my mouth. But they were true, even if they were wrong.

"No you don't Bill," she replied in a flat dead voice.

For a moment I thought to follow it up, to insist that I meant what I said and to make her know it. But how could I make her know anything? The lenses she wore in her inner spectacles were different from mine, so each of our points of view was distorted. Neither of us saw the truth. Anyway I didn't care what the truth was. I only wanted her to see my truth, but that would require the alteration of her private index of refraction. And how do you do that?

"Well," I said lamely, "there's not much more I can say, is there?"

"No," she replied quietly, "I'm afraid we'll have to accept the facts as they are. You are a public man and I am a private woman. And we don't mix."

94

I thought about this for a moment and then shook my head. It was no good thinking about it or shaking my head. This was no kaleidoscope. This was our life, our joint life, and there wasn't much left of it.

"Still you do have some consolation, Bill, don't you?"

A new note in her voice turned my head towards her. Gratuitous this, some new hazard to watch.

"Oh," I said enquiringly, "do I?"

"Remember you told me the rule-of-thumb method you used in your office? When a wife came to see you and complained that her husband wasn't sleeping with her, there were usually two alternatives. Either he was ill, or there was another woman."

"Well?" I said uncomfortably.

"You're not ill, are you?"

How many men, Samsons unwitting, break down the columns on which their peace of mind rests? No excuse for me. I knew or should have known, the fatal trap of the advocate, the question too many.

"And don't you have any consolation, Mary?"

A pause. Then mockingly: "I'm not complaining."

It had taken all this time to clear the decks. And Diggins was now very far away indeed. I felt my face flushing and clenched my hands. But I was able to control my voice:

"Don't you think you had better tell me a little more Mary?"

"There's no more to tell Bill," she said hurriedly. She was frightened. There was more to tell, too much more.

I sat down on one of the hard uncomfortable kitchen chairs. Not because I wanted to sit, but because my legs were giving way. This was something I hadn't bargained for. But why not? If I had a mistress, why shouldn't Mary have a lover? And why wasn't I angry? Why did I feel only sick and winded as if I'd been kicked in the stomach?

"I'm afraid there is more to tell, Bill," she said eventually. "I've been meaning to talk to you about it for a long time, but it hasn't been easy to find an opportunity."

I felt so ill that I could hardly hear what she was saying. And then I had to leave the room hurriedly. I was sick for a long time, coffee and sandwich sick all over the pan. And after I had stopped vomiting, I remember staring at the specks of bread and cheese and the dark brown coffee stain on which nuts of butter quietly rested.

When Mary came to find me, I was shivering all over, but I wouldn't go to bed. I knew I shouldn't sleep until I had got myself more under control. There were two things hammering in my head which I had to get out of my head if I were to sleep at all. I went downstairs to my room to deal with them.

One was the last conversation we'd had together about three weeks earlier. That had also ended in a row. Only then she had used different words. She'd been complaining of my neglect of her and the children, her perennial complaints, and then she'd said what I had thought was rather curious:

"I've had a pretty thin time with you Bill, one way and another. But I did all I could. I gave you everything I had to give and you threw it away. And now if I'm not what I was, it's your fault."

"Why should you talk to me of fault?" I had replied bitterly. "What matters is not whose fault it is, but how to put it right. I've heard you say that often enough. And I must say I find it hard that you should refuse to me the generosity you extend to others."

She had laughed: "You find that hard, do you? I also found it hard, but I learned to endure."

I had stared at her: "Why do you want your own back?"

She had looked at me thoughtfully: "I don't want my own back."

"Then what do you want?"

"What does it matter what I want?" she had replied impatiently. "What's more to the point is what I'll get," and her voice had crackled. "There's nothing for us to do. We're on a treadmill and we'll just keep on. You'll live your life and I'll live mine. Pathetic little Jimmy will ring you every time his unsatisfied wife beats him up. Sheila Smith will give you her hopeless progress reports every week. Mrs. Gray will 'phone to say her family are trying to get her into an asylum again. The briefless ones will keep asking us to dinner. And I shall have to answer the 'phone and say you're out and I don't know when you'll be back. Your friends must think you're never at home—not that you are much."

"Can you wonder at it," I had said savagely, "when all I ever

hear from you is criticism of myself and abuse of my friends?
You're just like my mother." The last words had rung in my
head. They rang until the lining of my head had felt sore and hot.
"You're just like my mother." And so she was and until that
moment I had never known it.

My mother had exercised her wit on every childhood friend
I'd had and I hated her for it. Every friendship I'd had as a child
and a young man had borne the wounds of my mother's tongue.
The War had fortunately taken me from my home and saved me
from my mother. And in that last conversation before my opened
eyes in the kitchen of a suburban house which my genteel mother
would have loathed, as I'd looked at my wife, I realised I had
married my mother.

That was one thing out of my head, accounted for. The other?
And the sick feeling came back. I couldn't deal with that tonight.
All I could do was to try and blot it out.

I put a record on the gramophone, Gounod's Funeral March
of a Marionette. The music whirled about me, covered, clothed,
pressed against me. I was Gounod's marionette. I had had about
as much control over what mattered in my life as a marionette.
And the music seemed to me then as Proust said music had
seemed to him, truer than all the books I knew. When the record
stopped, I telephoned Willie Vincent. The 'phone rang for a
minute or two and I had begun to think he was out, when a
woman's voice answered, a voice I didn't know.

"Hello," I said. "Is Willie there?"

"No," she replied, "he's out, I'm afraid."

I wasn't sure from her voice whether this was one of Willie's
women stalling for him. And so badly I wanted to talk to him . . .

"Look here," I said and I must have sounded rough and
urgent. "This is Bill Mortlock and I simply must talk to him.
If you tell him it's me, I'm sure he'll talk."

Her voice remained unrippled: "I'm so sorry," she said, "he
isn't here. He went out a little while ago."

"Oh," I said. And then I didn't say anything for a long time.

"Hello?" she said. "Hello?"

"Never mind," I replied as the raven said "Never more," and
rang off.

I tried to tell myself that this was how it always was, that there
never was anything to hold on to when the load was breaking

you except God, and what had I to do with God? I had destroyed him in too many arguments. I didn't need any crutch, I'd said. I wanted nothing from the great bully who having created a Universe, stood by and watched it degenerate into a mad-house. And now in my own hour of need, I knew that let any old idol crawl into the room at that moment, and even as his clay feet were smearing the carpet, I would have bowed down and worshipped.

Instead, I drank half a bottle of rum. What did it matter, I thought as I staggered to bed, where you found your Gods, in Church, in women or in drink? So long as you found them.

WEDNESDAY

I DON'T KNOW HOW I got to the office the next morning, but it wasn't until I was sitting at my desk and sipping Anne's friendly coffee that I stopped being a stone. As a child I had lived in the country and near the house, at the corner where the orchard met the drive, there had stood a large brownish-grey stone. I had befriended this stone which I much admired for its stoic qualities. It never complained when the rain dripped on it, when the hailstones bounded from it, when the snow buried it. Nor did it ever ask for help. It simply waited, always the same whatever the circumstances, superior to its tormentors because it never yielded to adversity. And I noticed that the tormentors eventually always disappeared, while the stone remained the same. It seemed to me then, as it seems to me now, that adversity is a temporary state so long as you do not budge from your position, so long as you endure.

When I was not at school, that stone was my best friend. Brothers and sisters might perhaps have shamed me into denying my friend, but I had none, and the gentle stone taught me its wisdom. And when the inconvenience of living depressed me, I crept inside myself and my friend folded his huge brown-grey bulk around me and made me safe. I was a stone too, although my body walked and talked and drew triangles on the blackboard. I was emotionally ossified until I felt ready to face the impact of living again.

This trick had considerably simplified my life, though I suppose everybody must have some kind of hiding place into which he can shutter himself. From the moment I had left my bed, I had felt nothing. It didn't work in bed and I had spent a sleepless night lying hunched in a corner, keeping as far away from Mary as I could, alternately angry with her and fearful for myself. But neither anger nor fear had changed my habits. And I arrived at the office late.

My head felt swollen and tender and at first I didn't think I was going to manage. But after I'd dictated the post and read the

Jarvis case, all that was left was a dull ache at the back of my head. Then the telephone started to ring.

"Good morning Mr. Mortlock," Joan said in a hushed, unusually subdued voice. No bush telegraph works faster anywhere than in my office. "It's Mr. Faulkner. He's tried to get you twice this morning already."

"Hello Harold."

"Hello Bill how are you?"

"I'm all right. How are you?"

"I'm fine Bill, except I think Reggie and I have come unstuck on a contract. Could you have lunch with us and talk about it?"

"Harold, I don't want to be unsociable, but you know how busy we are. Come over here. I'll give you an early appointment."

"But you've got to eat Bill. It'll save your time and mine if we discuss it over lunch."

I laughed. "Lunch with you Harold, takes three hours. Your lunches are very good but I'm sorry, I just haven't the time. Let me look at my diary." But it wasn't time. It was inclination.

The last lunch I'd had with those two had cost just over £12 and it still embarrassed me when I thought about it. They were expense account men and I didn't much care for the way they operated their expense accounts; it seemed to me a fraud on the community. So I was determined to refuse the invitation, courteously if possible, rudely if necessary. I had only accepted his last invitation because the restaurant had been close to the Charing Cross Road where I had for ages been wanting to look for a particular book. But he didn't know that. And anyway the thought of lunch with Faulkner, watching him chew his food with his front teeth like a sheep, was more than I could bear.

"I could fit you in on Monday at three, if that's any use to you Harold?"

A deflated voice said: "All right Bill, Monday at three." Curious, I thought, as I put the 'phone down, how it upsets them when one doesn't take the carrot, even when it's only a small carrot like a lunch. It couldn't have been because they wanted to save time by talking over lunch, because I was certain that they would spend less time in my office and on the journeys than we should have done over a meal. It wasn't as if we were even very friendly. No, I fancied that Faulkner was upset because he liked to be the boss in any situation in which he found himself. He felt safer like that. And you do get at least temporary control of a person if you buy him something, even if it's only lunch. For Faulkner to have to come to my office meant for him a surrender of his authority to me. He would have to come on my terms. And he didn't like it.

Anne came in. "Mr. Nixon's here," she said handing me the file. "And I've given Mr. Smithers an appointment for four. That's the only time you had today."

"Smithers?" I queried, "who is Smithers?"

"But I thought Mr. Gissing . . ."

"Oh yes," I interrupted. "Barlow's assistant. I remember now. All right, thanks Anne."

Nixon was a tall, powerful man, with big brown eyes and a large nose and thick wiry black hair, about forty. He had long black hairs trailing out of his ears. I found them rather disconcerting, though I think they were harmless. But they looked very sinister indeed.

We had first met over a Probate Action in which he'd been involved. Now he was consulting me about his wife. This was always happening. One day there would be nothing in the office except divorce.

He was trapped by his circumstances and by the kind of man he was. What made it worse was that his marriage had helped to make him the kind of man he was. He'd been married about ten years and there were no children. The marriage had been unhappy for a long time. His wife wouldn't sleep with him, would hardly do anything for him. I don't quite know what she did with her life or whether she had anything you could properly call a life. But I'd heard this kind of story so often before, that it was obviously true. I shuddered to think how many women lived like that.

For the last five years he had been keeping another woman. But now she had revolted and demanded marriage or else she would leave him. Before he could marry her, he had to get a divorce and that wasn't so easy.

What was he to do? The answer was obvious, wasn't it? He must strive for those conditions in living which would give him happiness. Anything else was failure. That's what Llewelyn Powys said. That's what I said.

"Yes, I agree," he replied, "but how can I strive for those conditions, if my wife won't divorce me?"

"She's changed her mind again, has she?" I asked.

He nodded. This was the third time that she'd changed her mind. He didn't look very unhappy about it. I didn't think he was very unhappy about it. He was by no means sure that he wanted to be divorced.

He was also frightened. Suppose he got a divorce and married the other woman? Marriage was different from concubinage, wasn't it? He really wanted things to stay as they were now and resented the pressures being put on him. Dividing his time among two women meant that he asked less from each, needed less from each. But suppose he only had one? It might place him too much in that one's power. And he didn't care for that. Then there was the question of money. His wife would get maintenance, a large share of his income, perhaps even a third. And money was security, money was love. Perhaps he'd better stay where he was where he could control the housekeeping, than move into what lay outside. Who could know what lay outside? At least with his wife he knew where he was. Ah, but he also wanted the other woman, he also wanted to be happy. How could he have it all? That was why he'd come, for me to wave my magic wand and make it work out right for him.

"I've been thinking," he said, his brow creased. "Perhaps it's really better for me to stay as I am. What do you think?"

I laughed: "How can I answer that?"

"Well if she won't divorce me," he said, "what can I do?"

I laughed again: "I agree," I said cheerfully. "There's nothing you can do."

He frowned. He was remembering his mistress's threat: "Yes," he said eventually, "but I can't go on like this indefinitely, can I?" His voice was querulous.

"Pity, isn't it?" I said.

He sighed and then he saw I was mocking. He was really a simple man and he smiled without guile.

"All right," he said. "Well what am I to do?"

"Your case isn't exceptional, you know," I said seriously. "A lot of men are married to women like your wife and they face the same dilemma as you. They're not happy with their wives and they've either got or would like to have, another woman. But often they can't cope with the guilt they feel towards their wives, when they think of starting again with someone else. And if they can, then they frequently resent the idea of paying maintenance to the woman who's made them unhappy. In your case, you've had a good working arrangement until now. Your wife doesn't mind you having a mistress, but now your mistress minds you having a wife. So you can't have them both. Well, you'll have to make a decision. Either get your wife to divorce you, or give up having a mistress, or get another one. They seem to be the alternatives."

"No," he said in a tremulous voice, "I can't give her up." He lay back in his chair, while the tendrils from his ears crept along his face. I kept telling myself that they weren't dangerous, but they looked so predatory that I had to turn away.

It seemed that there was only one alternative left, but we could do nothing about it, if his wife wouldn't divorce him. Sometimes I suspected that he hadn't even asked her, that each time he came, he made up another story. But we went on discussing his problem. It was all quite useless, I had no doubt, but he needed an outlet just as Mrs. Gray did. Only this time I should be paid for my services.

And also I was very much on his side. I thought that perhaps if he'd had some happiness from his marriage, if he hadn't been forced to squeeze every little he got out of his wife, if she'd been more open-handed, more open-hearted, more open-bodied, perhaps he would have risked putting all his weight on his mistress, and paying the accepted tribute to his wife. But then perhaps he wouldn't. How could one tell?

And if his marriage had really made him like this, then the marriage had done a good, secure job, because it looked as if he were going to be too frightened to break it up.

When he went, we had come to no conclusion. He found it impossible to come to a conclusion. The hazards were too great. Instead, he would return next month and we'd go over it all again. That would give him the illusion of doing something, without the reality.

Miss Jarvis was waiting and when Anne ushered her in, I saw what Henry had meant. She was accompanied by her mother, a great joint of a woman. Perhaps 'accompanied' isn't the right word, because throughout the whole interview, she said perhaps half a dozen words and then only after her mother had said: "Go on, answer him."

As they came into the doorway, I thought for a moment that Mrs. Jarvis wasn't going to get through, but she shook it off and came bounding up to me looking like a crumpled St. Bernard. She raised what appeared to be a plate and recklessly I plunged my hand inside it, half expecting it would never emerge. I was abruptly taken back to my childhood. One day I had gone into the kitchen and there being nobody about, I had put my hand inside a piece of unrolled dough, just to see what it felt like. I needn't have bothered. I would have learned the feeling when I came to meet Mrs. Jarvis. My hand was slimy and greasy when it was finally released.

Miss Jarvis didn't offer her hand. I said formally, "How do you do." But it was her mother with whom I could see I was going to be concerned, and she would require to be met with a professional manner. I squinted under my eyebrows at the chairs in the room and in helping Mrs. Jarvis off with her coat, guided her into the largest. By this time Miss Jarvis had seated herself.

I said in what I hoped was a highly professional voice:

"Dear me. This is a most unfortunate matter, Miss Jarvis."

"And so it is," her mother replied in a deep booming voice that reverberated around the room. "The poor girl is quite heartbroken."

I looked at the poor girl. She didn't look anything. "And," I went on professionally, "it is made more unfortunate by the appalling manner in which you have been treated, Miss Jarvis."

"Shameful," her mother said. "The poor girl hasn't slept since it happened."

There was no point in looking at the poor girl. I was perfectly certain that she did nothing but sleep, if only to keep her mother at bay. But this was undoubtedly the right stuff. Mrs. Jarvis was nodding briskly in encouragement. If only I could keep it up. "It would seem extraordinary, wouldn't it Miss Jarvis, if this man could behave in this beastly way, humiliating you and distressing your mother . . ." I paused briefly to gather my strength. Mrs. Jarvis was still nodding, but I was entering the shallows ". . . it would seem extraordinary if you could do nothing about it, wouldn't it?"

"Yes," Mrs. Jarvis said: "It would seem extraordinary, particularly after what that poor girl has suffered. I know," she said, shaking her head. "I've seen it." I deliberately kept my eyes away from the poor girl. "But," I ended, with a sinking heart, "extraordinary though it might seem, Miss Jarvis, I'm afraid you can't sue him for breach of promise and I'm afraid you can't keep his parrot."

"Can't," said Mrs. Jarvis. Then she said it again, as if she had never before heard the word. I looked at her. Her hair was cut in a fringe all round which made her face look wider than it actually was and it was too wide already. At the best of times, it would have looked several sizes too big for her skull and with that haircut, it was not the best of times.

"Can't: But Mr. Spencer didn't say that. He just said it might be difficult. And he never said we'd have to give the parrot back." She was aggrieved. Mr. Spencer was Henry, though it took me a moment to connect. When it did, I cursed him under my breath. How he must be cackling at the thought of this interview.

I put on my glasses and became judicial. "You see Miss Jarvis," I said, looking as always at her mother, and remembering what I had looked up in the books before they came, "you were given the parrot as a kind of engagement pledge. You weren't actually given a ring because you both wanted to save the money for your home. But the parrot served the same purpose as a ring, and an engagement ring and similar gifts are, in the absence of an agreement to the contrary, conditional gifts, the condition implied by the Law being that if the marriage doesn't take place, they must be returned. Unless of course the marriage is broken off by the donor. If your—this man had broken off the marriage without your consent, you could keep the parrot. Of course," I went on reflectively, "you could then also sue for breach of promise."

"But that's exactly what he did do, didn't he Joan?" said Mrs. Jarvis excitedly.

"Yes mother," said Miss Jarvis dutifully.

I hesitated. "But Miss Jarvis," I said doubtfully, "you broke off the engagement yourself. That's what Mr. Spencer's got written down here."

"But he made her. That great bully made you, didn't he Joan?"

"Yes mother."

"Who made her?" I asked. By no stretch of the imagination could I see Henry bullying her into breaking off her engagement.

"George made her of course," Mrs. Jarvis bellowed. "The man she was going to marry. Didn't he Joan?"

"Yes mother."

"How did he make you Miss Jarvis?" I asked gently.

Mrs. Jarvis snorted. "How did he make her? Why because of his treatment of her. He would argue with me and spend all his time talking to the parrot until it got on my nerves and I told him to get out and stay out. He only did it to insult us, didn't he Joan?"

"Yes mother."

I shook my head. "I think you'll have trouble if you keep this parrot. The man has threatened to sue and if he does, the Judge will probably order you to give it back. It would be cheaper and more sensible to give it back now, before he sues."

"Well," Mrs. Jarvis cried angrily, "so he has it all ways, does he? He plays fast and loose with my daughter, and then when he changes his mind, she can't sue him and he gets his parrot back too." She beat the arm of the chair with her fist. The arm gave a hollow groan.

I looked at Miss Jarvis speculatively. Fast and loose? But no, it was only too clear that George hadn't played fast and loose with Miss Jarvis.

At a signal from her mother, Miss Jarvis rose and I stood to face the two ladies. Mrs. Jarvis was still snorting: "I thought the Law was supposed to give justice," she said. "I don't call this justice. Why it's not even fair."

An interesting distinction, I thought, as I saw them to the door, but this was not the moment to pursue it. And Mrs. Jarvis relented at the last moment. "Thank you for your advice any-way," she said and thrust out her hand. I hesitated and then reluctantly I entrusted my hand to hers. After all, it was for the last time. I managed to get it out just as she manœuvred her daughter through the door to clear a space for herself. Thinking I was safe, I was surreptitiously wiping the slime on my hand-kerchief, when at the last minute she turned again to say Good-bye, and saw what I was doing. Hastily I pretended to be blow-ing my nose, but it was a difficult moment as we gazed at each other across my handkerchief. Finally she lumbered out without a word.

I handed the file back to Henry. "She wasn't very difficult,"

I said. He gave me the only admiring look I ever saw on his face. "Wasn't she?" he said wonderingly and I left him to wonder.

As I was dictating attendance notes of the interviews, the telephone rang. I barked: "Not now Joan, I'm dictating."

Joan was apologetic but insistent: "I'm sorry Mr. Mortlock, but Mr. Clacker is on one line and Mr. Leon is on the other and Miss Streeter has just rung off. And Ernie is here and says he knows you're in and wants to see you for just a minute."

She sounded so distressed that I laughed. "One at a time Joan. Mr. Leon first and then send Ernie in. I don't want to talk to Mr. Clacker and I'll ring Miss Streeter later."

Leon took no time at all. He wanted to make a will and I passed him on to George. I didn't want to speak to Clacker because Clacker would have taken a long time and made a lot of noise and I didn't feel up to it. He was a constitutionally angry man, a partner in a large firm and he'd been too big for his boots for a long time. He was also a bully and he worked on the theory that if he huffed and puffed for long enough he would blow your house down. One day I would get him to creep down my chimney and have a big fire waiting for him, but not this morning.

Anne brought Ernie in. Ernie is the porter of the building in which we have our offices. When I first came to the firm, I struck up an acquaintance with him and a couple of years ago he asked if I would advise him. I said I would, and I never regretted anything in my life more.

Ernie is a tall, skinny, bald man of about fifty. He has a lined, grey face and wears horn-rimmed glasses. But they lend him no dignity and merely disturb the line of his face. He is rather deaf and sometimes you have to repeat what you have said several times. He also repeats everything he says, in case you too are deaf. It is perhaps not surprising that he is rather an irritable man.

He was for a long time engaged in a state of bitter warfare with the woman who lives upstairs. She deliberately slammed doors and turned up the radio so that he couldn't talk to his wife. Her habits were indescribably dirty and she was cheeky as well. But unfortunately she paid her rent regularly.

For many a long hour I listened patiently to all Ernie's complaints about the woman upstairs. I advised him to apply to the County Court for a possession order. But he never did.

And then one day the enemy changed, and Ernie turned on his

wife. She was taking the dog to bed with her, he said, and this was depriving him of his rights. I had quite a job explaining his rights to him. Each time he came to see me now, he would tell me of his wife's latest enormity and refer to his lack of rights. And each time I would explain what the Law considers a man's rights to be. But he never asked what a man might consider his rights to be and I never told him.

I dreaded Ernie's visits. I never asked him to do any of the jobs he was supposed to do for us, because I simply could not bear any increase in his appearances. All sorts of expedients had already been tried with him, and everything had failed. If I were engaged when he called, he simply waited in his lodge until I went to lunch or was going home. I had found it easier to see him when he called. There appeared to be some mechanism in him that required release every two or three months. Sometimes he called at the end of the second month, sometimes at the end of the third month, but he never missed. Latterly, he had grafted a new pattern to the thrall in which he held me. On the last four occasions when he had come into my room, he had brought with him respectively a broken-down old chair, a set of table mats, a lamp shade and a cushion. On each occasion he had started the conversation by saying that he had made this chair, these mats, this lamp-shade or this cushion and I could buy it or them for £2. Always the price was £2. Then he began to discuss his wife and his lack of rights. Eventually I realised that I could cut it short if I bought his handiwork quickly. So I did, at £2 a time.

I had tried to stop him getting on to his rights by offering him the money straight away, but that hadn't worked. I had to hear the latest developments, but once heard if I paid up, I was free. Now I wasn't sure which I dreaded most, the awful interview or the rubbish I would have to buy.

Ernie came into the room. He was beginning to squint behind his glasses. Otherwise he was the same man.

"Good morning Mr. Mortlock." His manner was very respectful but he had nothing in his hands and I was rather suspicious.

"Good morning Ernie. You're looking well."

"I'm feeling rather tired as a matter of fact. I've put in most of me spare time on your bed."

"On my bed?" I said faintly.

"Yes, about a fortnight ago as you and Mr. Gissing were going home, I happened to hear you say that you'd soon have to buy a bigger bed for your boy because he was growing so fast. So I thought I'd knock one up to save you money."

I did vaguely recollect saying something like this to George but I was appalled at the prospect which now lay before me. I managed to collect myself:

"That's very kind of you Ernie," I said hopelessly. Without a word, he opened my door and from the passage he dragged in the bed he had knocked up. Now I understood why Joan had sounded so frenzied in telling me that Ernie had arrived. I looked at Ernie's work in silence. I had seen a few beds in my time, but I had never seen a bed like this. It consisted of four legs of wood, none of which was the same width or length. Nailed to the legs were four uneven, knotted, unplaned planks of wood, of different lengths with gaps varying between half an inch and three inches between them. I could see thick carnivorous splinters crouching on the planks, waiting for flesh.

Ernie was pleased with his bed. You could see that by the gentle way he leaned it against my wall, taking care not to cut himself on the heads of the nails projecting dangerously from the four corners.

I blew my nose to hide the horror which must have been written on my face. Perhaps I could pay him now and get rid of him. I said:

"That's a very fine bed, Ernie. How much do you want for it?"

"I knew you'd like it Mr. Mortlock," he said. But he didn't answer the question. Instead he remarked, his brow wrinkled as if he were about to impart some valuable information: "You know Mr. Mortlock, I've been thinking about me wife. I've been thinking about it all. I'm a man, aren't I and I'm entitled to me rights. So long as I haven't lorst me nature, I'm entitled to them, aren't I? Can't I make her, Mr. Mortlock?" He paused and licked his lips, while I shuddered at the thought of it. "What does the Law say I'm entitled to?" he asked, and as I was about to tell him, he interrupted with a wave of his arm and said mournfully, "I must just tell you what she's up to now."

And he did, leaving nothing out, and I, like some paralysed fly caught in his web, did all that was expected of me.

When it was done, before he could start again, I said hurriedly:

"I like that bed Ernie. How much do you want for it?"

I had expected him to say two pounds, but he said "Four pounds." It was too late to rebel, and meekly I handed over four pound notes and asked him to take the bed away until I could send someone to collect it.

"I knew you'd like the bed, Mr. Mortlock," he said happily. "It was on the tip of me tongue, yes on the tip of me tongue, to tell you several times, but I didn't. I wanted it to be a secret, a real secret." And he frowned, and began to drag the bed away.

George missed it as he put his head round the door, but he only just missed it. He watched Ernie carrying the bed along the corridor. He looked amused. I felt exhausted and terrified of what schemes Ernie might be hatching against the future. George jerked his thumb towards the disappearing bed:

"How much?"

"Four pounds."

"Gone up, eh? How much have you paid him altogether."

"This makes £12."

George began to laugh. "You'd better get Ernie his rights," he said. "Then he'll leave you alone."

"You think the bed's symbolic, do you?" I said suggestively.

He stopped laughing and sat down: "I thought you might like to know that I saw Hattie and told her roughly what we decided the other day. She didn't seem in the least concerned and when I'd finished, she told me that the share-pusher's come back, and she was so dreamy and vague that I could hardly get any sense out of her."

"Perhaps he scented some boodle under Harry's will," I said.

"That's what I thought," he replied. "But Hattie said he knew she had no money."

"Oh well," and I shrugged. "Let's leave it until the next instalment. There'll be one. There always is with that family."

I looked at him: "Anything else George? I've got a good deal to do."

"I came to ask if you wanted me to do any appointments for you tomorrow. I spoke to Anne and she said that if I saw Bird, she thought you could manage the rest. Can you?" He sounded kind. I was glad of it.

"I'll manage George." I could hear my voice coming from a long way away.

"Come on then," he said, getting up from the chair. "It's our sixth anniversary. I'll take you to lunch to celebrate."

"Not at your club, George," I replied, shrinking from the thought of it. "I couldn't face all that drink and all those jokes."

He smiled: "All right," he said, "no club."

As we were about to go, the telephone rang.

"It's Miss Streeter," Joan said in the neutral voice she used about Susan.

"Hello Susan," I said. "I'm sorry about last night."

"That's all right Bill."

"Dinner tonight?"

"That will be lovely."

"Be with you about eight."

"I shall look forward."

As George and I went out, he said:

"How are things at home?"

"Couldn't be worse."

He didn't say any more and we had a very good lunch.

AFTERNOON

When we got back, White was waiting for me. This was yet another who belonged to the great legion who wanted and who did not want to be divorced. As I looked through his file, I began to brood about it. Funny how it always seemed to be men. The Gibbons woman was rather exceptional. My experience was that a woman usually stayed where she was until she had an acceptable alternative and then she just cleared out. Children naturally complicated the pattern, but didn't destroy it. Children only qualified the meaning of what was an acceptable alternative. But generally it was the men who wanted more than they had, while the women bided their time. Still, as they were economically the weaker sex, there was probably nothing else for them to do.

I estimated that about half the people who consulted me for divorce really wanted a divorce. Invariably they had plans and other spouses waiting in the offing. But it was the people who had no other plans, no alternative, who came to take the last desperate step and didn't want to take it. Some people seemed able to take off their marriages as they took off their clothes. I wasn't much concerned for them, though they helped to swell the coffers. It was the others who were my people, and they kept coming in increasing numbers. More and more, I was beginning to see that if you put all your emotional capital into your marriage and it didn't succeed, you couldn't get it all out again to try with somebody else. You were stuck. There was no back and not much forward. It was probably just as well that most people didn't put everything into their marriages. Perhaps they hadn't got much to put. Which was lucky. There was enough unhappiness about as it was.

What to say to White? Unhappily slumped in the chair, he was in debt all round, and he thought he'd be able to concentrate and put it all right if only he got rid of his wife.

"Have you thought about going back together?" I asked tentatively. His eyes had the boiled look which comes from too much drink.

He shifted in his chair. "Not since the last letters you wrote to her."

"I wrote those letters about the hire purchase debt," I said.

"Yes, but I told her that once that was settled we could talk about other things."

"What other things?"

"You know," he said pushing his legs out at me, "reconciliation and things like that."

"Did you mention reconciliation to her?"

He was silent for a moment. "Well no, not exactly," he said.

I looked at him. "But you want a reconciliation, don't you?"

He drew his legs back and pushed them out at me again.

He didn't want me to talk like this; he wanted to push me and my suggestions away.

"What's the good?" he asked wearily. "She's got all the men she wants. She doesn't want me."

And there we were. Back, always back to the need for purification. Take away her men, clean her and hand her back and I'll have her. But don't ask me for any effort. I can't make it.

I leaned back in my chair. Really what was I to do? He wouldn't do anything to help himself and I couldn't live any more lives. Not any more.

"Mr. White," I said, "we can probably get you a divorce; we've got evidence of adultery; but honestly, I don't think it will do you any good. Every year there are 30,000 divorces, about ten per cent of the marriage rate. If you can cope with being just another casualty, we'll go ahead. But I don't think you can cope. Can you?"

He squinted up at me: "I'll manage," he grunted.

"But you don't manage," I replied. "You're falling to pieces. You've changed your job three times, your house is falling apart over your head, you're in debt all round. And all this since you left your wife."

"Well what did you expect me to do?" he said angrily. "Stay there while she slept with her boy friend?"

"I don't expect anything," I replied quietly. "I'm only trying to put it to you before it's too late. There must have been a reason for her to fly off the handle like that. Can't you talk to her about it?"

"What am I supposed to say?" he grumbled. "Why were you

unfaithful to me? Aren't I good enough for you?" Then he gave me an unfriendly look and said: "Well, what would you have done?"

What indeed? I remembered what I had done. Telephoned Willie Vincent and played the gramophone and then shut it all in a secret compartment in my head marked 'Fragile. Do not open.'

I shook my head to clear it. He was quite right; no more fine phrases, no more bogus help. I would do what he said he wanted me to do.

"All right Mr. White. You want to go ahead. I'll get the Petition drafted."

But he didn't want this at all. He put his feet firmly, heavily on the ground.

"Wait a minute," he said hastily. "You didn't say what you'd have done."

I made an effort. For how long can one go on making efforts? I said slowly:

"I would arrange to meet her in a neutral place, in a hotel lounge or somewhere like that and I would try and make her see that I loved her and wanted more than anything to live with her. She says you didn't spend enough time with her or take her out, and that you weren't proud of her. Well reassure her that it is going to be different. If she's any feeling for you, you'll soon know. And if she hasn't, well, then you may have to get a divorce. But surely it's worth a try."

Cautiously he was turning this over in his mind. Then a snag struck him.

"But how do I know she'll come?"

"Write her a warm friendly letter."

He smiled sadly. "I can't write to her at all."

"But surely you have to write when you want to see the children," I replied.

He shook his head: "I always tell the children when I'll see them next."

"And you never have to alter the arrangements?" I asked.

"That's the reason why I never alter the arrangements," he replied.

I was caught up in it again. He must be very tied to this woman not to have been able to write to her in two years.

"I'll draft a letter for you," I said, and I wrote a simple love letter without a word of love in it. I was very good at this kind of thing, manœuvring behind words for other people. I had drafted dozens of letters like this, sometimes with agreeable results. In order to induce a meeting, all you had to do was to try and make the recipient feel the heartbreak behind the simple unadorned words. If there was love or sympathy on the other side, there was usually an immediate response. If not, at least there would be curiosity. It only failed when there was hurt or bitterness there, and usually it was the hurt and the bitter who came to see me.

I handed him the letter. "I hope it works," he said.

There was hardly any time to look up the law before Smithers came, and I was still looking at the book when he was shown in. He was a young man of twenty-five and he was frightened. He had every reason to be. He and a man called Robinson were charged with committing an act of gross indecency with each other contrary to Section 11 of the Criminal Law Amendment Act 1885. They were also charged under a local bye-law which made it an offence punishable by a fine of £5 for any person in a street or open place to which the public have access, to commit or attempt to commit an act of indecency with another person. I did what I could to put him at his ease and then got down the facts. They followed very much the usual line, only this time the story was that there had been no mutuality, but that the other man had indecently assaulted him by grabbing his penis. I said:

"When they took you to the police station, did you make a statement?"

He hesitated: "I was so upset that I can't remember what I said," and he wetted his lips. "Shouldn't I have said anything?" he said.

He was frightened enough and the milk was spilt anyway. "I don't think it matters," I said and went on:

"Do you know whether the other man made a statement to the police?"

"I don't know, I'm afraid."

"What's this other chap look like?"

"Well he's about forty, red ugly face, broad, shabby clothes, running to fat. . . . I can't think of anything else I'm afraid."

"He looks respectable?"

"Well no, not very."

I leaned back in my chair and inspected Smithers. He was a pale young man, hair, eyes, skin all looked as if the colour had been drained out of them. He also looked as if he could be queer. Over the last six years I had had over a dozen of these cases and in every one of them the client had given the impression that he might have been homosexual. Which didn't of course prove guilt; it could have meant that the Police only looked for a certain type, but it was odd and it made the chances of the defence slimmer than they need have been. It was also a point you could never put to the man himself.

I said as he watched my mouth:

"You have a clean record—never been in trouble of any kind before?"

"No, nothing." He was clasping and unclasping his hands and for a terrible moment I thought he was going to crack his knuckles, but he didn't.

"Mr. Smithers," I said quietly, "before I go any further, I want you please to understand that I accept everything you have told me as the truth." This much he was entitled to. It was little enough. But he looked as if he needed it.

He nodded. "Thank you," he said gratefully.

"The difficulty is, of course, that it isn't enough to convince me. We have to convince a Magistrate and perhaps also a jury."

He nodded again.

"I don't know what the prosecution evidence will be, but experience has taught me that it won't be the same as yours. Almost certainly we will hear two stories tomorrow, and the Magistrate will have to decide which is true, if the case stays in the Magistrate's Court."

He shook his pale head and said loudly: "What I've told you is the truth. If the police say otherwise, they are lying."

He said this with an assurance we both knew he didn't possess.

"I know how you feel Mr. Smithers. This is the dilemma which confronts every Court. But it isn't that the Police are lying; that's altogether too simple an explanation. You can't remember now what you told the police, but if you'd tried to explain what happened, the other chap—what's his name?"

"Robinson."

"Yes, Robinson, would presumably have denied that he was

interfering with you. If the Police had believed what you told them, they would have charged Robinson alone. Instead they've charged you jointly though that may have been a precaution, to see what comes out in evidence." I paused briefly. "This is of course pure conjecture. It may be that you were so confused that the Police don't know that Robinson assaulted you. You may have been too upset to make yourself clear. It's often like that," I said kindly, as he began to sag, "particularly in this kind of offence." Then I said briskly: "Anyway I shall get to the Court early tomorrow to have a word with Robinson's Solicitor to see how he's going to plead."

"You mean Robinson may plead guilty?" he whimpered.

I looked at him for a moment. The interview was getting out of hand, going at his speed not mine. And he wasn't in a state of mind to control anything. So I brought the conversation to an end abruptly and became professional.

"I'll deal with that in a moment. But first I must explain the alternatives open to you. There are two charges against you, one serious and the other not so serious. The serious charge cannot be dealt with in the Magistrate's Court. That Court can only hear the evidence and if there is a prima facie case against you, the Magistrate will commit you for trial, probably to Sessions. The less serious charge can be dealt with once and for all at the Magistrate's Court. Now the Prosecution is sometimes prepared to drop the more serious charge, if a plea of guilty is entered to the lesser charge under the bye-law. If you plead guilty to the bye-law, the maximum fine is £5, and that will be the end of the matter. But I should tell you that a plea of guilty means a conviction for indecency registered against you for the rest of your life." And I stopped to let it sink in.

"And if I plead not guilty?" he said quietly.

"Then you will be committed for trial on the more serious offence and you will be tried before a Jury." His face was working and he kept passing his tongue over his lips until he felt sure enough of his voice to go on:

"What are the chances," he asked, "of getting off, if I am committed for trial?"

"It's difficult to say," I replied, "when I don't know what the prosecution evidence will be or what Robinson will say or even what you've told the Police, but I'd reckon that you'd have a fifty-fifty chance. I could perhaps be more definite after I've heard the evidence tomorrow."

"And if I'm convicted at the other Court," he whispered, "am I likely to go to prison?"

"Well the Act provides that a sentence of up to 2 years can be imposed, but for a first offence without particularly nauseating circumstances, I should think you'd get off with a fine. But you do see, don't you," I said warningly, "how very difficult it is to assess these things when we haven't heard the evidence?"

He nodded.

So far so good. Now we could deal with the trimmings.

"You asked me earlier whether Robinson might plead guilty," I said. "I couldn't answer that question until I'd explained the alternatives to you. You see that?"

He said, "Yes," but I was pretty sure he didn't, so I went on.

"One reason why he might plead guilty is to keep the case in the Magistrate's Court, pay £5 and be done with it."

"But how can I plead not guilty if he's going to plead guilty?" Smithers asked in a hurried, panicky voice.

"It complicates matters of course," I said, "but there's nothing to stop us pleading not guilty, whatever Robinson does."

"It will look peculiar though, won't it?"

"No, I don't think so. I think you can safely leave that with the Judge. After all our case is that Robinson assaulted you indecently. The Judge will realise that Robinson might plead guilty to avoid going into the witness-box and being cross-examined." There was another reason why I thought Robinson might want to plead guilty but I didn't mention it to Smithers. If the Court accepted Smithers' story it would mean not only an acquittal for him, but also that the police might later charge Robinson with indecent assault. So Robinson had at all costs to prevent Smithers' story being accepted, because it didn't look as if the doctrine of autrefois acquit, autrefois convict would help him. By pleading guilty, he would throw his weight behind the prosecution's evidence and that would almost certainly be enough to prevent Smithers being believed. And Robinson only risked a fiver. Unless he'd done this kind of thing before. With some Judges that could mean prison and people don't usually take risks like that. So our best hope really was that Robinson had been convicted of indecency before. There was no point in telling all this to Smithers. It would only frighten him still more. Anyway it was all surmise. But I decided to talk to Counsel about it and let him tell Smithers if he thought it necessary.

For the moment, what I had to do was to get Smithers ready to face tomorrow. As I looked up at him, he said frantically: "He'll plead guilty. I know he will, and then what will I do?"

"Let's wait and see," I said calmly.

But his pale face had gone grey. I had a brief longing for some happy people to come into my room and stay happy, but sooner or later their faces all became the same colour.

His head began to shake from side to side. He said:

"It looks pretty black, doesn't it?" and I could feel the weakness surging up in him.

Then he raised his head and looked at me with wide eyes. I had seen those eyes before. He was going to ask me to make up his mind for him. And I didn't want to. I felt old and tired and full of failure. I wanted to ask someone to make up my mind for me too. But who was I to ask? "What do you advise?" were the words he spoke, but that wasn't what he meant. He wanted me to decide for him. But even this pale ghost was too much. I was too encumbered, too heavy. I couldn't take anybody else on my back. But always one had to make the effort and I tried to make one. I felt it in my backbone as I spoke:

"It would be cheaper and easier for you to plead guilty tomorrow," I said, "but my own view is that an innocent man should never plead guilty. It is of course sometimes done, particularly in the Magistrates' Courts because it saves time and trouble. If you plead guilty tomorrow, you'll be fined £5 and that will be the end of the matter except for the stigma of the conviction for indecency. If you plead not guilty, you'll be tried at Sessions, and that means you'll have to wait two or three weeks before the case comes up for hearing. You'll get bail of course, but it's nasty having to wait so long. These are the alternatives. I can do no more than put them to you. But only you can make up your mind what to do."

I didn't look at him. I didn't want to look at him until he had come to a conclusion. I knew it was hard, but it wasn't my problem. The silence went on until it began to roar in my ears. So I raised my head and we looked at each other and I heard myself saying the words I had been determined not to say:

"If you want my advice; if you are innocent, you should not plead guilty."

And he replied with a determination which I could feel flowing out of me as he spoke:

"Yes, I will plead not guilty."

The tension between us snapped and I felt relaxed and unwound. Smithers looked as if he felt the same. "Have you told your family?" I asked.

He nodded.

"Good. There's bound to be something in your local paper but that can't be helped. It's best to be frank with the people who are important to you and the rest can think what they like. Don't you agree?"

He nodded again.

"Try not to worry," I said. "I know it's difficult, but you've got to be at your best tomorrow. And above all make sure you sleep tonight. If necessary, take a pill."

We shook hands. Even his hand felt lighter.

Then I cleared my desk and went off to Susan.

As we were eating, I studied her. She was not beautiful, perhaps not even attractive as women go, but I thought she had the quality which the Chinese call jen. Mencius describes jen as the expression of the heart, a definition I sometimes found meaningful and sometimes not. But it was Susan's empathy which entitled her to the virtue jen and, what was perhaps more important from her point of view, to my inconstant affection. With her I had no need to explain or identify myself; she required no personal formulation from me. And so there was no reckoning. It meant that with her, I could always relax. Here was no enemy. This evening she wore an air of inner tranquillity which I found greatly soothing. And I was thinking that perhaps this quiet woman was all I needed when I heard her laughing softly. I turned to her:

"I've been talking to you for the last five minutes and you haven't heard a word, have you?" she said in her gentle voice. No resentment, no clamant demand for attention; she knew she had all the attention I could give. And she seemed to think it was enough. I warmed to her and to the soothing unobtrusive voice. And then I began to laugh myself. I remembered the car I once bought because I liked the sound of its hooter. That car had served me pretty well. Perhaps voices were as good a test as any other. Perhaps I should buy Susan?

"Why do you laugh?" she asked.

"I was wondering whether I should buy you."

"Surely the problem is whether I could buy you," she replied.

And then the moment was gone and I was turned inward again picking the scabs off. But just in time she said: "Let's go, we haven't got very long." And we went back to her flat.

As we were lying in bed, I told her what the week had been like, all the week except Mary. "You don't have much of a life do you?" she said. "All you seem to get is what you can squeeze in between your cases."

There came a hammering inside my head. The door behind which I had pushed all the things I didn't want to face, began to give. Again I heard Mary saying: "Now I know you're no good to me. Our life together is just something you manage to squeeze in between cases." Even to the same words, even that! I concentrated on the door. If that door burst, I was finished. Above all, I had to keep that door closed, until I was ready, if I were ever ready. I pressed against it with all my might until I felt it was safe. Then I relaxed, feeling suddenly light-headed. "I do all right," I said eventually. And then I thought of an answer, the complete answer. "If you think I like working so much," I said in a mock severe tone, "why is it that I can't get up in the morning? Why do I always arrive late?" And I lay back content.

"Because your blood sugar's too low," she replied instantly.

"Nonsense. Only because I'm lazy and reluctant to face the outside world."

She laughed: "You don't believe that do you?"

"Of course I believe it," I said indignantly. "It's true. I hate getting up."

"Yes I know you do. But if you raised your blood-sugar level before you got up in the morning, you'd have no trouble getting out of bed."

I looked at her angrily. I shouldn't have been surprised by this high-powered technical talk. Her father was a scientist and sometimes it proved too much for her. But it always did surprise me. It seemed so unlike the rest of her.

"And how do you raise your blood-sugar level before you get up?" I asked.

"Anything with sugar will do," she said, "but I always keep a tin of barley sugar by the bed and I suck a couple just before I want to get up."

"You're missing the point," I grunted: "I never want to get up."

She snuggled up to me:

"I'll give you some to take with you and you see if it works."

A long time later, I told her about Smithers. She said: "Do you think he did it?"

"Of course I don't."

"Tell me darling," she said, moving my head until it rested on her breasts, "what do you do when you think your client is guilty."

"I never think he's guilty, unless he tells me he is," I said, sighing gently. I was pretty sick of that question. Every time a layman got hold of you outside the office, this was the question he always asked. And now it was being asked in bed.

"But surely after a man has told you his story, there must be times when you don't believe him. What do you do then?"

I thought about this. It was curious how I had never learned a formula to answer it. Sometimes I quoted Erskine defending Tom Paine. I had learned about two hundred words of the speech for the purpose. Sometimes I cited Johnson's famous passage to Boswell.

But neither would do for Susan. So I said slowly:

"You see it doesn't happen like that. When a man asks me to act for him, he expects me to present his case in the best way I can. That's my job and that's all I do."

"But what would you do if he told you he'd done it and asked you to make up a defence?" she asked.

"I wouldn't act," I said, "it's not a solicitor's job to make up defences. I believe you can act for a man who's told you he's guilty and let him plead not guilty because the Prosecution has to prove his guilt and in legal theory a man is innocent until his guilt is proved. But I don't think I would act myself in a case like that. It would be too worrying. I should tell him to go and see somebody else. But I shouldn't think that sort of thing happens very often."

I bent down to kiss her. Her brow was furrowed. I began to wish I'd never mentioned Smithers.

She straightened her body. She was resting her head on my

arm. Now she turned it towards me, her face serious. "But suppose a man consulted you and told you his story and you didn't believe a word of it. What would you do then?"

I hesitated and tried to choose my words carefully by peeling the substance from the attitude, layer by layer. But it was harder than usual because there still lingered in my nostrils the hot sickly sweet smell of her body and I didn't altogether care for it. So I said finally:

"Well, apart from the occasional lunatics every Solicitor runs across, I'm afraid it doesn't work like that, not in civil cases at any rate. A man's case may be weak and I would tell him so, but that doesn't make him a liar. And sometimes he forgets things or the details don't absolutely hang together and this I would point out to him and try and jog his memory. But that's about all. You must remember," I went on, "that we don't do very much crime. I daresay if I were in the Criminal Courts every day, I might think differently."

She moved her head away impatiently and raised herself on her elbow. Her breasts danced with the movement. She had a beautiful bosom, smooth compliant breasts, quite unlike Fanny Trenchant's. Fanny manœuvred her breasts as a captain his ship, consciously, deliberately, aggressively. 'Look at us,' they demanded. 'We're worth seeing.' But Susan's were gentle and warming. Thinking to keep her quiet, I paid her a lavish compliment.

"You are a Goddess among women, Susan, and I worship at your beautiful breast."

She smiled and fell back on the pillow and I rested my head on the soft flesh.

But she said: "No seriously Bill, what do you do when you don't believe your client?"

It was my turn to move away. Why was it so important to her, for God's sake? It was an attitude, a habit of mind, a professional technique. It wasn't my business to go around believing or not believing. I just had to present a case. What was so wrong about that? Journalists are paid to voice their employer's opinions, to present their employer's case. Accountants spend their time finding ways for people to avoid tax. The so-called commercial morality of the business world was unspeakable. Why pick on lawyers?

I rested on my elbow and looked at that calm face. I could

hardly believe that I had possessed her, could hardly remember the struggle, her cries, her ardour. She looked too much her own woman. I made another effort.

"You see darling," I said, "it's like this. When I listen to the story a man tells me, my main concern is to make sure that it will sound right. That's because the truth sometimes doesn't sound true. So I would do my man no service by allowing myself to be persuaded one way or the other. What I have to do is to present the case so that it sounds right."

"How do you do that?" She was amused.

"Well I really think it's a matter of experience. Putting the man at ease, explaining the issues to him, telling him what's relevant and what's not, testing his story and seeing that it hangs together with his witnesses' stories, and making it seem right generally. Then when I've got him a good barrister I've done about as much as any craftsman can hope to do."

I lay down again and for a while there was silence between us. But for some reason she couldn't leave Smithers alone, or was Smithers only a symptom? Why was it that she couldn't keep quiet tonight? And why tonight, when all the inflammable matter in my head had only just been stored away? I couldn't afford to be jarred tonight. Anything might happen. And where was the empathy I had given her so much credit for? It was always like this, I thought wearily. When you needed something in somebody, you put it there. It wasn't really there at all. Only the reflection of what you wanted. That's why the people you loved were always better, kinder, more thoughtful than anybody else. Because you wanted them like that, they had to be like that. Until you found out.

"Do you think he'll get off?" she asked.

"I don't know," I said, "it depends so much on which Judge we have, who's on the jury, how the evidence comes out and what kind of impression he makes. It's all a lottery you know, particularly in these cases."

"Why in these cases specially?"

"Because they usually take place in public lavatories and I have views about public lavatories. Some of them are constantly watched by the police and are very good places to avoid. I would myself rather ruin a pair of trousers than go into certain lavatories."

"Really?"

"Yes, really. Some lavatories are used as picking-up places by queers. The police know about them and keep a sharp eye—too sharp, I think."

"But surely the police wouldn't deliberately make up a false story?"

"I don't know what the Police would or wouldn't do," I replied. "A police constable is like the rest of us. He's fallible. What you've just said implies that every person charged with an offence on Police evidence must be guilty. Too many people take that view and it's wrong. A policeman can make a mistake like anybody else and from one point of view, there's more reason for a policeman to make a mistake. In this case for example, the policemen who thought they'd caught my man out, may have been doing lavatory duty on and off for weeks, and never found anybody to catch. Then they went into this lavatory and saw something which was undoubtedly suspicious, so they made an arrest. There may have been a quite innocent explanation if only they'd listened to it. But they wouldn't listen. They may have been too inexperienced or too excited," I said charitably.

"Why should they have been excited?" she asked.

"Don't you think it would be exciting to make an arrest when you're doing what's mostly a boring routine job?" I said.

Then I went on: "I don't know what the evidence will be tomorrow, but it won't be what my client says. The police will no doubt quite honestly say what they think they saw, but it won't be exactly what happened in that lavatory a week ago, because now nobody knows exactly what happened. Each person will give his impression of what happened and the constables will be fortified by their notebooks. And everyone's account will be coloured, my man's, the other man's, and the Police. Because each will be giving evidence of facts and the facts don't exist any more. Between the facts as they happened and the evidence as it comes out at the Court, lie the differing refractive qualities of each of the protagonists. And they differ because their density differs. And so what goes into each of them comes out of each of them at a different angle." As I stopped there came the hammering in my head again. This was the analogy I had used to myself about Mary last night. I grew angry. I wasn't going to have Mary interfering every time I thought about something which

I'd once applied to her. I returned privately to my thought. But even if that difficulty were overcome, still there was the insuperable obstacle that we have only the inexact shape of words to clothe the forms created in our minds. Proust's commentary on communication was never far away from me: 'Between oneself and the rest of the world one has the barrier of a strange language.'

"But anyway," I said fiercely, "coming back to the facts" (the faith which people seemed to repose in facts always goaded me) "by which you mean the recollections. Tomorrow or at Sessions we'll hear two or three sets of facts, all conflicting and yet everyone, except perhaps the other man, will think he's telling the truth. And they will. They'll be telling their version of the truth, their truth. Which is about as much as you can expect from any man."

I drew a long breath, "Satisfied?"

She smiled a secret smile. "Oh yes, a long time ago."

"I thought you didn't like conversations like that," I said.

She snuggled closer to me: "That was before I knew I could buy you. It's different now." Then she said: "You have a little sleep and I'll wake you when you have to go. You've got about an hour."

But was it different now? My last thought before I went to sleep was of Mary. Wherever I was, with whomever I was, my last thought was always of Mary. And I knew with a great bitterness that tasted like gall in my throat that infidelity was useless; each act of adultery only made the bond of my servitude more taut. I wanted my wife and I wanted her on any terms. But I tightened my arm round Susan's thighs and went to sleep for my hour.

THURSDAY

It wasn't Susan's barley sugar which got me out of bed the next morning. It was the telephone. Henriette also seemed to be in the house for some reason I didn't understand.

"Monsieur," she was saying as I peered up at her, "M. Clark wishes to talk with you on the telephone."

As I opened my mouth to speak, the barley sugar rolled against my teeth. I took it out and wrapped it carefully in my handkerchief against the next experiment.

"Hello Freddy," I said at last.

"Hello Bill, you're not in bed are you?"

"No, no, I'm just leaving." I always carried this off rather well, I fancied.

"Oh good. I thought I'd ring you at home because it's so difficult to get through to you at the office. Your number's always engaged." He was complaining, so I said:

"I'm very sorry Freddy, we've been trying for ages to get some more lines."

"Norah's in rather a stew about Paddy," he said. "She wants to come and see you."

Paddy! I thought, Paddy! Who the hell was Paddy? It sounded as if Paddy was alive so I said cautiously:

"What's Paddy done?"

"He's bitten someone."

Ah, Paddy was a dog. I got more confident.

"Who's he bitten?"

"The postman."

"Badly?"

"No, torn his trousers, scratched his leg and generally shaken him up. We brought him into the house and gave him a drink and Norah sewed up his trousers. He's just gone. Norah thinks Paddy will have to be destroyed and she's wailing all over the house. She says she wants to come and see you at once. Can she come this morning?"

The last words woke me up completely. I couldn't have

127

Norah wailing all over my office. Somehow she would have to be kept out, at any rate until she'd stopped wailing. So I began tentatively to feel my way:

"Tell me Freddy. I can't remember offhand because I know so many dogs, what's Paddy?"

"Paddy's an Alsatian," he said in a hurt voice.

He thought I should have remembered.

"Christ," I said. Suddenly I had remembered. Paddy was a despicable creature whose teeth were always bared. I would have been quite glad to have arranged for Paddy's swift and painful destruction but it would have meant seeing Norah. Paddy would have to live.

"Freddy," I said in a kindly tone, "you know that Alsatians have a reputation for being treacherous." I could hear fluttering at the other end of the telephone, so I went on hurriedly:

"I know that Paddy's an angel, of course, but . . ."

"A more gentle, docile animal than Paddy you couldn't find," he said loyally. "He isn't really like an Alsatian in character you know." His voice got very confidential and slightly mad. "He just looks like an Alsatian."

It took me several seconds to get my breath back.

"Do you know why Paddy bit the postman?" I managed to ask.

"Well we'd been playing with him just before the postman came and he was a bit excited I suppose, and when the door was opened he went flying out."

I kept the sight of that terrified postman conscientiously out of my mind as I said:

"How old is Paddy?"

"Three."

"Has he ever bitten a postman before?"

"No."

"Anybody else in uniform?"

"No, uniforms don't attract him."

Then I hesitated and plunged. I was afraid of the answer but I couldn't properly avoid putting the question.

"Has he ever bitten anyone before?"

Silence at the other end and my heart sank. Norah was going to wail at me.

At last he said "No," rather dubiously, "you couldn't call it a bite. Once he knocked over the greengrocer's boy as a joke and

128

the boy got scratched as he fell, and of course he's always playing with the children in the neighbourhood."

"Do the children object?" I asked in a noncommittal voice.

"The mothers complain sometimes until they realise it's all in fun," he said, "but everybody round here loves Paddy. He's so full of life."

As he went on about Paddy, I heard myself singing in my head "Everybody round here loves Paddy." It sounded like a corny pop song. When he'd finished I said:

"Freddy, every dog's entitled to one bite, even Paddy. Perhaps I should say particularly Paddy. But see that he doesn't have any more because it might be hard to prove that he isn't really an Alsatian. And if I were you, I should give the postman some money to get himself a new pair of trousers and be very nice to him."

"You think it'll be all right Bill?" He sounded doubtful.

"On what you've told me, I should say you're all right, but if there is any trouble, let me know."

"They can't just take Paddy away?" he asked.

"No Freddy, they can't just take Paddy away," I echoed and rang off.

I rushed into the bathroom feeling fine. I sang "Everybody round here loves Paddy", at the top of my voice. And I went on feeling fine until Henriette knocked at the door and said: "Breakfast Monsieur."

"Where's my wife, Henriette?"

"She is shopping Monsieur. She has left a note for you in the kitchen."

I knew from her face what there was for breakfast, but I had to see what was in that note.

As I went slowly into the kitchen, I didn't feel fine any more. The note said: "*Please* be early. The Andrews are coming for dinner. The usual telephone calls last night *and* Willie Vincent."

But I couldn't face the breakfast and left it lying on the table as I rushed past the astonished Henriette.

Out of the house I felt better at once, blood sugar or no blood sugar. And relieved. I'd been frightened by Henriette's appearance and that note. But it was all right. I had a coffee and still arrived at the Court early.

I met Smithers in the lobby. He was alone and palely loitering. But he was glad to see me.

"How are you feeling?"

"Fine," he said and smiled.

I left him to go and telephone Anne to find out if anything had happened, but nothing had. As I struggled out of the booth, I nearly knocked a friendly policeman over.

"Who's sitting?" I asked.

"Grumble," he replied, grinning.

"Oh dear." I didn't fancy Grumble much. He was rude, abrupt and usually in a foul temper. It did mean that I shouldn't be kept hanging around the Court all day because he generally got through his lists quickly. But still I didn't fancy him much. I had hoped it was going to be Barndale who sat alternately with Grumble. Barndale was everything I thought a Magistrate ought to be, a gentle, kindly, courteous man with a nice face. I know people can't help what sort of faces they have but many of the men and women who find themselves in a Magistrate's Court have never been in trouble before and they are very often terrified. A quiet voice and a kind face can make a lot of difference.

I found the solicitor instructed by Robinson, a heavy taciturn man called Swish whom I'd never met before. He wouldn't discuss the case with me at all and I was driven to questioning him.

"You going to plead?"

"Certainly not. We're fighting."

"Your chap been convicted before?"

He gave me a long searching look which told me what I wanted but he said:

"Why do you ask?"

"No particular reason."

Then I said: "Hadn't we better see how far our stories tally?"

"Well what's your story?" he asked.

As we were talking, Chindle came up grinning. We stopped talking. Chindle was a young barrister.

"Hello," he said. "I'm prosecuting you." And he beamed all over his charming fresh face.

"That's nice," I said and introduced him to Swish.

"You're prosecuting him too," I added.

Chindle continued to beam. He was a nice young man and he was doing his best to make a good impression. If he succeeded we might send him work. Alas, he had no wit, so he was forced to beam until he could think of something to say. To save him from effort, I went over to Smithers and told him that Robinson was fighting, which cheered him up.

"You think it's because he's been convicted before?" he asked.

"I should think that's very likely," I replied and went into the Court to wait.

I know there are newspaper columns specially devoted, not to say dedicated, to what goes on in the Magistrate's Courts every day, but for myself I know of no more depressing place unless it be a public lavatory. If you really want to see what our society does to people, you have only to go into a Magistrate's Court and listen. Every time I spent a day in one of these Courts, I gave heartfelt thanks that my practice lay elsewhere. It wasn't that I objected to the punishment of crime; the big and the small time crooks got what they deserved for all I cared. But the squalor and the unhappiness and the aloneness of so many little people, squashed and humiliated out of shape by the pressures of our society—this I couldn't stomach. I resented the circumstances which had removed dignity from these people, which in turn had caused them to behave without dignity.

There was Grumble sitting up in his chair dispensing justice. He did it thoroughly and as efficiently as his overcrowded lists permitted. I allowed him this, though I did it grudgingly. He was a wizened little man with bright beady eyes behind pince-nez and an enormous nose. With brighter plumage he could have passed for a short-sighted toucan.

"Two pounds," he said and caught my eye. He frowned and looked the other way. This was something, I thought. Normally he refused to notice me until I had got to my feet and then he only conceded me the right of audience in his Court with some distaste. I have sometimes sat in his Court and not known I existed until my case was called, but today he had admitted I was alive.

As I was drawing faces on my pad, I heard a commotion. I looked up to see Grumble in one of his furies. The contours on his face were changing as if some terrible implosion had occurred. Finally he thundered to the shaggy little barrister who was on his feet: "Mr. Paint, you're doing your client no good by taking this line, no good at all. Now let's get on."

I hadn't heard what the fuss was about. It was almost bound to have been trifling. Encounters like this were always going on in Grumble's Court and people told me that eventually they got used to them. Grumble bore no malice and a minute after the outburst things were as normal, except for the quaking Accused who feared the worst and the poor young man by my side now reduced to a jelly. I knew exactly how he felt. Grumble had done the same to me the first time I had ever appeared before him.

Even now I could remember the weakness at the knees and the fluttery insides. I had been defending a young man who had stolen a pair of shoes. It was a first offence and he had pleaded guilty. I had intended to make a very short speech in mitigation, but Grumble kept interrupting me until eventually I lost all understanding of what I was saying and went on and on, too frightened to stop in case I'd left anything out. It was one of my worst moments, worse than anything that had happened to me in the War. When things got bad in the War, you fainted or ran away or hid, or at the worst you died. None of these alternatives was decently open to me that day in Grumble's Court. I don't know now how I stopped, but I well remember Grumble's brazen glare at me as he said to my trembling client: "Your learned Solicitor's plea hasn't been of great help to you. . . ."

Petrified, I had sat there all through the orthodoxy of Grumble's views on the sanctity of other people's property, expecting a terrible sentence, but finally the young man was bound over. When I had recovered some days later, I realised that if Grumble had done anything but bind over or fine, we could have appealed, but at the time I felt ill in every part of my body. So I knew all too uncomfortably how it was with the man sitting next to me. And his poor client probably felt a good deal worse.

Then I remembered I hadn't seen the Clerk about our committal to Sessions. I wrote him a note. "Re Smithers and Robinson. No objection to us going to Sessions rather than the Bailey is there?"

The Clerk read the note, smiled and shook his head. That was all right then. I tried to keep every case I could out of the Old Bailey, because I had found that the words "Old Bailey" had a paralysing effect upon people. Not that the trial would be any fairer at Sessions, but the client wouldn't be dead with terror.

Just after twelve-fifteen our case was called on. Chindle lumbered to his feet.

"May it please your Worship, I appear for the Prosecution and my learned friend Mr. Mortlock appears for the Defendant Smithers and my learned friend Mr. Swish appears for the Defendant Robinson." Chindle spoke in a midway voice, not too quietly for Grumble to cup his hand to his ear and not too loudly for him to say he wasn't deaf.

The Clerk read the charges and Chindle briefly opened his case and called his Police Constables. Both appeared to be very young, a sure sign of approaching middle age in me, but they were quite sure of their facts. They had both seen mutual masturbation between Smithers and Robinson. I felt rather sympathetic towards them because they were both so certain of what they had seen in a not very well-lit lavatory, over Smithers' shoulder a week ago. But neither Swish nor I cross-examined; there was no point in giving our defence away at this stage, especially as the defence stories were going to conflict.

After the Clerk of the Court had read over their depositions to the Constables, he gabbled Rule 5(4) of the Magistrate's Court Rules which he knew by heart. It should have sounded impressive because the words and substance are impressive, but he'd said them so often before that they didn't have any meaning for him or anyone else.

"You will have an opportunity to give evidence on oath before the learned Magistrate and to call witnesses, but first do you wish to say anything in answer to the charges. You need not say anything unless you wish to do so, but you have nothing to hope from any promise and nothing to fear from any threat that may have been held out to induce you to make any admission or confession of guilt. Anything you say will be taken down and may be given in evidence at your trial. Do you wish to say anything in answer to the charges?"

I got up and spoke my first words: "My client pleads Not Guilty, reserves his defence and calls no witnesses in this Court." Swish got up and said the same.

Both Accused were then committed for trial at the next Sessions and granted bail on their own recognisances and with relief I bowed myself out of the Court.

It had just gone one o'clock. I went into the office where

Smithers was filling in the form and shook his hand. He was overcome with gratitude. I couldn't think why.

On my way out, I bumped into Chindle.

"Lunch?" he suggested.

"Where?"

"There's a pub round the corner," he said.

We went to the pub. Chindle was a big, personable, cheerful man who laughed "Ho-ho-ho" as friendly giants are supposed to do. He talked about his cases and I listened to his cases. We had nothing else to talk about because he was the kind of man who says to you, "What are your interests?" Questions like this constipate me and I find I have no interests at all. Not that it mattered, because Chindle told me his, and his were motor cars, trams, aeroplanes and everything else mechanical. I felt rather like Mme. de Sevigny, deprived of solitude without being afforded company. Except of course that she hadn't got cases to discuss.

By two-thirty I was back in the office and the next hour I spent on the telephone dealing with Joan's list of messages. After I had dictated to Anne, I remembered Willie Vincent.

"Ring Mr. Vincent will you Anne? Tell him I'll call in to see him tomorrow evening if that's convenient."

And then I went to tell George about Smithers. He was sitting at his desk chuckling to himself and all the red-faced men on the walls seemed to be grinning as well.

"What's the matter?" I asked. "Another funeral turned up?"

George looked at me reproachfully. I always think that George's reproachful face is very funny. And I burst into laughter.

He said coldly: "Funerals are not funny."

I pulled myself together. He was the senior partner after all. "You looked very pleased with yourself as I came in," I said. "What's up?"

George looked undecided for a moment. Then he thawed. "Beeton's just been in," he said grinning again. "He's got another invention he wants to patent."

"What's he done this time?"

"Well I'm really not very clear about it, but he says that it's about time the drudgery of the housewife came to an end. All this washing-up, he says, it's quite unnecessary. He also talked a lot about women's rights and said that this new invention would give women a square deal at last."

"Interfering bastard," I said. "What's he got to do with women's rights? Anyway, how does he know that women even want a square deal?"

"He's entitled to support women's rights Bill, and his idea of a square deal for women is as good as yours or mine."

"I'm sick to death," I bellowed, "of all this bloody cant about women's rights. Women don't want rights. They want love and emotional security and if they've got those, they can do without the rest. They want a man and a home and if they haven't got those, equal pay and votes aren't much compensation. And I reckon a good many of them—the normal ones I mean—have begun to see it. I only hope it's not too late," I ended morosely.

George's grin was so huge that it was beginning to overlap the sides of his face. I could see he was goading me. I allowed myself to be goaded.

"I used to believe in women's rights," I declared, "but not now. I'm against any further assimilation of the sexes. We're merely turning women into second-rate men. And I'm all for women being women. I want them different from men, as different as they can possibly be. I want to see a healthy, lusty, sensual society. The Greeks had it. The Greeks made sensuality the whole basis of their life, and with their sensuality went an exaltation of mind to make a culture which has never been surpassed. There was no guilt, no shame in their sensuality. It was clean, honest and dignified. That's what I want to see. I'm also for men going about with clubs—I speak metaphorically you understand—and dragging women off to their caves. I despise these squalid creatures who get their pleasure by rubbing themselves against women in tubes and by footy-footy in cinemas. That seems to me a degradation of both sexes. Men should exult in being men. They should proclaim the phallus!"

I noticed that I had raised my arm as I said this and I was really feeling rather extraordinary. The red-faced men on the walls had paled and looked as if they were huddling together. George was sitting hunched up in his chair. I couldn't see his face, but I could guess at it. So I let him have a last burst to pay him out for goading me:

"Can't you see that women aren't our companions; they're our prey. They enjoy being preyed upon and we enjoy the preying. It's the natural order. It's also very exciting and very beautiful. So let's leave it alone."

George's room was a changed place. Nobody walking in at that moment would have felt it to be a Solicitor's office, whatever it may have looked like. The atmosphere was heavy, primitive and brutal. Almost, I could smell musk and hear the sound of pipes.

Neither of us spoke for several minutes. I found I was breathing rather quickly and I could hear George's breathing. Then he sat up in his chair, very red-faced. And as I looked at him, the excitement faded away and everything fell back into place. It was hard to see George except as a Solicitor.

I heard myself saying: "How exactly does Beeton propose to end the housewife's drudgery?" and I was surprised how normal I sounded.

"He's invented some kind of dining table," George replied in his usual tones. "Apparently the food is poured into cups let into the table. As each course is finished, you press a button and an automatic steam jet cleans the cups and there you are ready for the next course. No more washing-up."

"What about bones and things like that?" I asked.

"There's a sort of automatic ejector for those. They're taken straight into an incinerator and burned."

"I don't fancy that much," I said after a while. "Do you?"

"Well no, I don't," he replied. "I was thinking of my beautiful Chippendale table. I'm not having cups let into that."

"Surely it's not feasible," I said. I was thinking that we had enough gadgets already without a shining enamel monstrosity sitting in every kitchen.

"I don't know," George answered. "With Beeton anything is feasible, except we can be fairly sure it won't work. He's going to let me see the specification, but I think he only came in to gloat because we laughed so much at that kettle of his. Do you remember?"

I did, and we both laughed. Beeton had come into the office a year earlier and told us that he wanted to patent an invention which could make tea and coffee separately at the same time. He did a number of mysterious things and then plugged a kettle into the electric point. In five minutes it had blown up and each of us had ruined a suit with a filthy mixture of tea leaves, coffee grounds and other unknown materials. Beeton had gone away infuriated.

"Anyway," George said. "He's gone to see his patent agent and we shall only hear more of him if this invention works, but it won't."

"Well I hope not. And I hope to God he doesn't have another go at automatic boilers," I muttered.

George began to cackle: "I shouldn't worry," he said soothingly, "the boiler blew up too."

"Yes I know it did, but only after a fortnight. And it might work next time."

"Why are you so concerned about boilers?" George asked.

"Because boilers periodically drive the men of England, not to mention the women, to distraction. Just when you're comfortably settled in for the evening, you have to go and fill the boiler. And that usually means a journey into the cold. But first you have to rake it. That always ruins my temper for the evening and if miraculously I'm still cheerful after that, the next stage which is to remove red-hot clinkers, finishes me. All these manœuvres are accompanied by a female catterwauling, usually justified, because a film of filthy dust has settled on everything. And the bloody thing's always out when you want a bath. I reckon that boilers cause more bad temper in men than anything else in the home, except women. And if Beeton gets on to boilers again and abolishes washing-up as well, the divorce rate will drop by half. And what happens to our practice then?"

"Yes, I see what you mean; I'll try and keep him off boilers," George said sensibly, but as he scratched his nose he went on: "Still the more time people have on their hands, the more likely they are to get on each other's nerves. So perhaps the divorce rate will stay the same."

"George," I said earnestly, "this isn't like you."

"Oh well," he replied, waving his hand vaguely, but he looked uncomfortable. There are some things perhaps one oughtn't to say, even in jest.

Then he said: "Well, what happened?" He was cracking his knuckles, so whatever it was that had happened, was serious, demanding careful attention.

"Happened?" I echoed.

"Smithers."

"Oh yes. Nothing much. He's committed for trial at Sessions."

"What did the Police say?" he asked soberly. George had a wholesome respect for the police. An Establishment man, George respected all our institutions.

I shrugged: "What did you expect them to say? That they made a mistake? They gave the usual evidence." Then puffing myself up, I looked solemn and said in a policeman's voice: " 'I saw the Defendants facing each other, holding each other's persons in their hands, rubbing them vigorously and looking into each other's eyes.' " I began to laugh. "Persons! what a word to use."

But George was looking worried.

"What's the matter George?"

"Barlow asked me what the chances were of getting Smithers off. I said that if he were innocent, the chances were very good."

I laughed: "Did you George? Pray tell me, what's being innocent got to do with it?"

He looked at me rather cautiously: "You don't think he did it Bill, do you?"

Suddenly it wasn't funny any more. "I'm quite sure he didn't do it, but it's not very easy you know. None of these cases are."

And as relief began to glow on his face, I went on: "Don't tell Barlow too much yet because we've got a long way to go. I'll brief Somes because he's about the best man we can get for this kind of case and we'll see what he advises. Smithers says he spent the evening with his girl friend. That means she'll have to give evidence; not nice for her, but she'll have to do it. Then the constables don't look to me as if they'll stand up to a tough cross-examination. On the other hand, we can only say they're mistaken and not that they're lying, because if we lost, an attack on the police could mean prison for Smithers, if anybody like Jorkins were trying the case. And I suppose there's always the long shot that one of the jurymen or someone he knows has been accosted in a public lavatory. That might get us off by itself."

George nodded: "All right Bill, I won't tell Barlow anything for the moment." But I noticed he was still cracking his knuckles.

I had intended to leave the office earlier than usual. The arrears were piling up, but the Andrews were coming and I didn't want any more trouble with Mary. The arrears would have to wait for the week-end. But as I was leaving, Vingtot telephoned from the station. He had just arrived from Paris as he always did, without warning.

I telephoned Mary to let her know and then I went to the station.

"What have you come for this time?" I asked.

"I have arrived to learn English," he said.

"But you speak English beautifully," I replied. I meant it. He spoke with a charming euphonious accent.

He shook his head and moved his hands.

"I have this heavy accent," he said deprecatingly.

"How long are you staying?"

"Four weeks," he replied. "I have arranged a course."

"A course?"

"Yes, with Professor Pumper," he said proudly.

"Who's Professor Pumper?"

He stared at me. Then he laughed. I could see from his face that he had decided that this was the English sense of humour. "Of course you know Professor Pumper," he said, and I half expected him to dig me in the ribs.

For a moment his lips moved silently and then he went on: "You are pulling my legs," and laughed again.

"No, I'm not. Who is Professor Pumper?"

He frowned. Was this still the English humour? But perhaps not, because I wasn't smiling. He began to get excited.

"You don't know Professor Pumper? All over the world Professor Pumper is known as the chief English Professor who teaches English phonetics. In France everybody knows Professor Pumper. Is it possible that you do not know him? No, no, you are joking."

"No, I don't know him. I've never even heard of him. But why should I? I don't want to learn English phonetics."

Vingtot smiled. This was surer ground. This was the English humour again.

"I'm sorry you want to lose your accent," I said. "You've got a good working knowledge of English but you'll never learn to speak like a native, unless you live here and perhaps not then. So why go to all this trouble?"

"I must learn your idiom," he said.

"But you know that so often these people who are good at

languages are good for nothing else. You think. How many good linguists do you know who aren't also the most terrible bores?"

He appeared to think. Then he said cheerfully:

"Ah, but they were bores always. And I am not a bore, so I will not become a bore just if I speak a good idiom."

I gave it up. "Where are you going to stay?"

"The course begins tomorrow," he replied. "They will tell me when I go."

"I expect they'll put you in a hostel with the others. But wouldn't you rather stay with us?"

"I will ask tomorrow," he said.

When we arrived at the house the guests were already there. Mary was a bit chilling but I was glad to see the Andrews. Tom was a thickset man of average height, who looked shorter and older than he was. Fair, full-faced, warm and friendly, he was a most companionable man. He made an odd contrast to Vingtot, who was tall, thin, sallow and bald.

Nancy Andrews was a tiny person with an aggressive vitality which I found exhausting. She had a face like the slow loris, but thin and sad, and in it the golden brown eyes swam like anguished pools. She also had the easy grace of that creature, and like the slow loris she had never been tamed. She had Slav blood in her somewhere and life with her must have been very curious. She was all the things that Tom was not, mistrustful, wary, shrewd, aware and probably fey. I believe she used to go to fortune-tellers a good deal but had lately given it up. Or that's what she said. And she was so sensitive that it hurt you to watch her antennae curling about the room and withdrawing abruptly at too sharp a touch.

While we were eating, I asked whether anybody had heard of Professor Pumper the famous English phonetics teacher. Nobody had. I had expected Vingtot to intervene, indeed had started the conversation to enable him to intervene, but he said nothing. I expect he was absorbing the English idiom. And then the conversation got on to marriage and divorce. I suppose this happens to every lawyer, but I found that it was almost impossible to spend an evening with anybody except perhaps one or two very close friends, without some aspect of the Law turning up.

"Had any interesting divorces lately, Bill?" Tom asked. I searched my mind. I was off-duty now and I didn't want to get involved in anything controversial. Anyway, they only wanted a peg on which they could hang a general conversation. I thought of Victor Charbles' case which was on tomorrow. Nothing could possibly be more ordinary than that. And it would give them a peg and leave me alone.

I told them the facts briefly, without names. Names were never mentioned, nor was anything else which might identify the people concerned.

"You mean," said Tom, "that this chap's been maintaining his wife all this time?"

"Yes."

"But she cleared out, you said. Why should he have to maintain her?"

"He doesn't have to maintain her," I replied patiently. "He chooses to maintain her."

"Suppose it had been your client who'd deserted his wife, then he would have had to maintain her, wouldn't he?"

"Yes, then he would have had to."

"I can't myself see," Mary said intervening, "how it makes any difference who leaves whom. The woman's got to live and she can't easily get a job while she's got the child to look after."

Nancy took her up. "But I can see," she said. "I'm rather shocked by the way women behave here. It seems to me that they're prepared to break up the home all too lightly." She paused. Then she said: "Nor do I understand why adultery is so highly regarded in this country. I was brought up in France and I'm sure that the divorce rate isn't nearly as high there as it is here. Yet the men of France commit adultery and get drunk and behave badly just as often as they do here. Oftener I hope. I don't think Englishmen have much talent for adultery."

"It's all right Tom," she said soothingly, as he raised his eyebrows. "I haven't been making enquiries myself." And then she went on: "But a Frenchwoman doesn't, in spite of all her husband's misdeeds, gather up her children and run away and get maintenance into the bargain. No, she stays and keeps the home going and if she does go, she doesn't reckon on her husband keeping her."

"But Nancy," Mary replied. "If two people just aren't happy together, surely it's best for everybody if they separate."

Nancy laughed. It was a droll sound without mirth.

"Really Mary," she said. "What sort of woman is it who doesn't need to belong to a man? Every marriage has got its imperfections and it's no answer just to run away from them. It's a woman's job to make the marriage work and if it doesn't, it's her fault. I think myself," she said with emphasis, "that English women could do with a little more of the endurance which continental women seem to have."

There was a long silence. We were evenly divided. Mary and Tom, Nancy and I, and not so much in opinion only as in temperament. We all looked at Vingtot. His response was oblique:

"The divorce rate in France is very high also," he said. "I do not know of course whether it is higher than here." He shook his head. "But it is very high."

"Don't you think M. Vingtot," Nancy said, "that the home is guarded much more carefully in France, that people try and keep it going at all costs?"

"At all costs?" He shrugged. "Certainly it is true that if a husband and wife are not happy together, that does not mean divorce. There are many considerations, religion, family, children, property."

After a pause he went on: "And naturally there are consolations."

The word bored a hole in my head. But Mary didn't seem to have noticed and she replied without irony, without any implication privately directed at me.

"That seems ugly to me," she said. "If the home is unhappy, it's bad for everyone, husband, wife and children. And it doesn't concern anybody else but them. And to keep a bad home going, with the husband sneaking off to his girl friend and the wife to her lover, seems to me thoroughly demoralising. Better to separate, I would say."

Vingtot was looking at her in astonishment. But here was no English humour, only the humourless English social code. If it's bad, smash it up, even if there's nothing better. There ought to be something better.

We'd had these arguments before. Tom used always to be on Mary's side, but the maintenance problem had clearly troubled him.

"But Mary," Tom said, "suppose the husband can't afford to keep two homes going? If Nancy and I split up and I had to maintain her, I shouldn't have enough money to marry again and she and I would both have to live separately in discomfort, whereas together we live in comparative ease."

"We won't split up, Tom," Nancy said, "because it's my job to keep the home going and I'll keep it going. And if I fail as your wife, so that you want to spend your evenings drinking and whoring, I don't see that I've any business to complain. I shall still have to keep the home going. And if I get sick of it, then I don't reckon you have to maintain me. I expect you to keep me while I do my part but when I cease to do my part, you don't owe me anything."

"Isn't she a fine wife?" Tom said admiringly.

Mary didn't think so. She said tartly:

"Why should women put up with drunkards and woman-isers?"

Nancy turned on her: "Because if you thought for a moment, you'd see that when a woman is successful as a wife, her husband doesn't want to escape from her—to drink or fornicate," she paused and then said slowly, "or work."

Mary went pink, but she fought back.

"But surely what each of us wants is to be happy and if you're not happy with the man you marry, you're entitled to get away and start again."

Nancy swivelled her body and looked directly at Mary:

"Mary, you keep talking about being happy as if it were the end of all living."

"Isn't it? Shouldn't it be?" Mary asked quizzically.

"Who told you that it should?" Nancy demanded.

Mary shrugged. "Well if happiness isn't the aim," she asked, "what is?"

"I should have thought there were many things," Nancy replied, "and life itself is surely enough of an aim." Abruptly she turned her attention away from Mary. I could feel Mary's relief. "Have you never thought," she said to the table at large, "why it is that the values of our society are commercial? Why do we have this kind of society where everything is bought and sold?" Answering her own question, she went on: "I used to think it was an accident, that we might equally well have had something else. But I see now that it was no accident. Our society reflects us. That's how we are. Because for us as well, in all the aspects of

143

living, in the most secret parts of ourselves, everything has its price, everything has to be paid for." She paused to look at us. Everybody was looking vague, wondering what was coming next.

"Of course," she said comfortingly: "you don't realise that a price has to be paid until it's more than you can afford. Then suddenly you see that a price has always been exacted, but that formerly it was within your reach. And now it isn't." She turned back to Mary: "And what is one to do, Mary when one doesn't like the price?" she said mockingly. "Does one run away? I believe in the commercial world, people generally try very hard to avoid bankruptcy, don't they Bill?" She was back at me. "Don't they try and come to an arrangement with their creditors?"

"Well yes," I said, "decent people try and compound with their creditors unless the mess is too bad. Then they go bankrupt."

Nancy smiled at Mary, who was looking so crushed that to clear the air, I told them about Mrs. Jarvis' short-lived attempt to start an action for breach of promise in the name of her daughter.

"Don't you think the Law favours women Bill?" Tom asked.

"You mean because of breach of promise cases?" I said. "Well no, I don't. Theoretically a man could sue a woman for breach of promise if he wanted to."

"But men don't, do they?" Nancy said.

"No," I replied, "they don't. But that's got nothing to do with the Law. That's because women usually haven't got any money, so they're not worth suing. And because a man would feel ridiculous if he did. But mostly I suppose, because men and women are different."

"I wasn't thinking of breach of promise," Tom interposed. "I was thinking generally how much more favourable the Law of England is to women than it is to men."

"Well," I said doubtfully. "This subject has got a long history you know, and if the Law's now leaning in favour of women, it leaned the other way for long enough."

"Yes," he said impatiently, "but you just look at what a man has to put up with. First there's this crushing millstone of maintenance around his neck if he happens to make a mistake in marrying someone and there's a third of his income gone. I suppose that means that a man who marries three times is finished, because each of his wives takes a third of his income."

144

"No," I interrupted, "it's a third of the joint incomes, but if there are children. . . ."

"I believe," Tom went on firmly, "that whether we are living together or not, I am by Law obliged to support my wife. But she isn't bound to support me, however rich she may be." And he looked up.

I opened my mouth to enter a caveat, but he went straight on, so I closed it again.

"I believe," he continued, "that I am responsible for her debts until I put some sort of notice in the paper saying I won't be responsible any longer."

"It does you no good," I returned quickly, "to put a notice in the paper. That's quite useless. The law's a bit complicated on this subject, but broadly . . ."

I didn't get any further. Tom was plunging on:

"Then I'm liable to pay tax on my wife's income, even if I never see a penny of it."

"Yes, but you can be assessed separately if you wish," I objected.

"That's a fat lot of use," he replied. "Ultimately the husband has to pay."

"And then back to adultery," he said. "If I commit adultery with Mary and you sue for divorce you can claim damages against me as Co-Respondent. But I've never heard of damages being awarded against a woman Co-Respondent."

"That's quite right. You can't get damages against the Woman Named."

Mary took a hand in the conversation. "I can quote examples to you," she said, "where the Law grossly favours the man. If a woman saves money from her housekeeping, it belongs to her husband, doesn't it? You yourself told me that some ridiculous Judge said so," she exclaimed, turning to me. "I don't see how that favours women."

"Yes, that's true," I agreed, "and I think the decision is a bad one. But I must say that on the whole I agree with Tom that the Law does rather tend to come down on the woman's side. And I think the Law's right to favour women because economically a woman is usually still at a disadvantage and it's for the Law to redress the balance."

"She's not only at a disadvantage economically," Mary said. "In a man's world she's at a disadvantage throughout."

145

"I should have thought that a man's world would have been the best possible advantage a woman could have," Nancy said and caught my eye. Her face was alight with interest, fevered, intense. I was curious to hear what she was going to say.

"Has it ever occurred to you why the Law favours women?" she asked.

We all looked at each other.

"The first thing," Nancy said, "that a foreign-born woman notices when she comes to England, is the men."

We all laughed, all except Vingtot. He was too deeply involved in the idiom all around him.

"Yes," she went on, "but I don't mean it like that. What I mean is, she notices that the men here don't look at her as she is accustomed to being looked at. At first she thinks something is wrong with her, but then she realises that it isn't her, it's the men themselves. On the Continent, a man's admiration can send a woman's morale sky high. Here where her morale is always fighting a losing battle with the weather anyway, she gets no help."

"There are plenty of lecherous men in England, Nancy," I said.

"I don't mean that," she replied impatiently. "I mean that the men in England aren't really interested in women, they don't usually feel comfortable with them. They'll have a meal with them and sleep in the same bed with them and occasionally make love to them, but they don't really like women. They don't think of women as people. Of course the women don't find it strange because for most of them, men are Englishmen. But I know that women here feel isolated, inadequate, as if they don't really belong. And they're right. In England a woman is only half alive. She can have no idea what it's like growing up in a society where she's fully accepted, where the men know how to treat her as a woman."

"Well," Mary said coolly, "and what's all this to do with the Law favouring women?"

"Because," Nancy replied mockingly, "we're back to the price which has to be paid, whether you know it or not. Because men have taken away from women what belongs by right to women, they feel guilty and their unconscious guilt feelings are reflected in their institutions, one of which is the Law."

Then she turned to me: "And that, Bill is also why women have demanded what they call women's rights, of which you so justly complain. Because the men here refused them the place to which they were entitled they've been given compensation. As always, you see," and she was mocking again, "the trouble with English women is English men."

"Well," I said. "I'd go some of the way. Women have sometimes told me professionally that they could have stuck anything if only their husbands had needed them. I suppose a good many women must think that men can manage by themselves. They're quite wrong of course, but the women don't seem to know it."

"Of course they don't," Nancy replied. "The men look and behave as if they don't need women, so the women feel squeezed out, as if they weren't real."

"Well, why don't they do something?" Tom asked.

"Perhaps they haven't noticed," Nancy replied smiling.

"Haven't noticed?" Mary echoed tartly.

"Well," Nancy exclaimed, spreading her hands innocently, "What about the coelacanth? That's been around fifty million years and nobody noticed that."

In the difficult moment which followed I turned to Vingtot: "What do you think Vingtot? You represent an ancient and distinguished culture and a different order of things. Come, tell us what's wrong with the Anglo-Saxon world?"

He looked up, his brow furrowed and we all waited expectantly:

Then he said: "This unconscious guilt feeling which Mrs. Andrews was reflecting. I cannot see what it means to the Law."

We all laughed: "Nor can I, Vingtot," I said.

"Now, no more nagging," Tom said, looking directly at Nancy. "I never go anywhere without you. So let's have no more complaints."

"Yes, but I've tailored you," she answered. "I've wormed my way into your life at so many points that you can't avoid me."

"Well why can't other women do the same?" he asked.

But nobody answered until Mary said: "Perhaps fear of a rebuff, perhaps pride, perhaps lack of understanding. Perhaps it's because the women here simply have no idea what men are like, and the men certainly don't have any idea what the women are like."

"Don't you think," I said, "that perhaps the self-interest of men and women often collides at too many points to make a working arrangement really possible? And that this becomes truer the higher up the scale you go?"

"That may be so," Nancy replied. "I suppose if your main interest in life is playing chess, you solve your problem by marrying a chess woman. But if you like a good many other things as well and you also have equally well defined dislikes, then it must be more difficult to arrive at a happy marriage. Unless," she added, "you've got a good deal more tolerance than most people seem to possess."

"Well I think women are wonderful," said Tom.

I agreed: "So do I. But let's talk about something else."

And everybody laughed again.

Because it was a cold March evening, we drank coffee round the fire and as we all got warmer, so the two women who had been so edgy a few moments before at the table, relaxed. We tried to make Vingtot talk but all he would say was: "I am obliged to listen," and we left it at that. For a time we talked idly, and then Nancy turned her long pointed face towards me. Golden flecks glittered in her eyes and I had barely remarked the changed mood denoted, when she said: "I've given your name to a girl friend of mine, Bill. I hope you don't mind."

"What does she want my name for?" I grunted. I felt indolent as if from too much lying in the sun.

"She wants a divorce."

I didn't answer. This sort of conversation happened to me about once a fortnight with different people who always used the same words. "I hope you don't mind Bill", they would say. "A friend of mine wants a divorce and I've given him your name." Why should they think I would mind? But that's what they said. Sometimes I thought it was strange how many people I knew who lived on the threshold of other people's divorces. But it was very good for business.

I could feel Nancy's insistence, though she wasn't saying anything. I never knew anyone whose silences were so loud. I preferred her when she talked. Then you could relax, but when she was silent, you had to be on your guard, covered up, with your vizor down, because then she was everywhere, smelling everything out.

So I said against my will, because I didn't want to talk and I didn't in particular want to talk about divorce, but I wanted to get her away from me, to leave me alone:

"What sort of divorce does she want?"

"You remember," she answered, "you once said that the divorce laws of this country could have been made by Jehovah?"

"No," I replied. "Somebody else said that and I quoted him."

"Well anyway you said that they worked best when they were applied to primitive people and crude situations—the brutal husband, the erring wife, the lusty unashamed appetites."

"Yes, that's true," I said. "It's easy to get a divorce against a man who bashes his wife. It's easy when the man and woman openly live loosely. But the Law makes no provision for the quiet destruction husbands and wives practise on each other. The wounds don't show. Desertion as a ground for divorce has made it easier, and removed some of the need for deceit, but even so the true state of affairs between husband and wife too often never comes before the Court. If it did, I fancy there would be fewer divorces."

"I've known the girl who's coming to see you since I was a child," Nancy said earnestly. "She was the happiest person I ever knew but now she's in a pretty desperate state. She told me that it had never occurred to her that she would ever want to spend her life with anybody but her husband. And then she said, one day it was all gone and she saw that happiness is gossamer and breaks at a touch, that the beautiful things that had been between them weren't there any more. So she tried very hard to get them back, because she hadn't got anything else to hold on to until she discovered that trying's no good. She said she suddenly saw how life really was and she didn't care a bit for life as it really was. And for the first time she realised that although she had always complained that life was too short, now she knew it was too long." She stopped, almost with a sob and said: "That's why this girl wants a divorce."

"I'm afraid," I said when I had recovered, "that if she's not more specific than that, she won't get one."

Nancy didn't answer directly. I felt her pressure on me momentarily released and I looked at her. She was gazing in my direction, but not at me. Her eyes were fadingly, rather blearily amber. She was perhaps a little drunk. And then Vingtot took a hand in the conversation. He said, leaning forward: "But what you have related so beautifully is not the story of your friend. It is the story, the tragedy of everybody. We all start life like Gods to impose our terms on the Universe and then slowly we find out what life is really like until finally we are swept off the stage like like . . . like bluebottles."

And indeed when Nancy told the story of Berenice and John it was commonplace and trivial, a story whose theme I had heard a hundred times. The woman expected of the man what he hadn't got to give her. He didn't understand the things that she wanted, so he gave her other things. She couldn't understand why he was giving her things she didn't want and not the things she did want. And so it went round.

I could understand that Berenice and John didn't see what had happened to them, but why couldn't Nancy see it? I shook my head. "You've sent her to the wrong man, Nancy. I can't do anything for her. It's not a matrimonial offence not to live up to your wife's expectations. It might be in America, but not here, not yet. As you yourself pointed out, we practise Jehovah's laws here. And I should have thought a psychiatrist might be more useful to them than a Solicitor."

Nancy smiled her sad smile: "You've missed it Bill. The details of what has happened between them don't matter, nor that he buys her a fur coat when all she wants is to go for a walk in the country. The only significance in the story is that what Berenice sought in John, he no longer has to offer. Their marriage is at an end."

"But Nancy," I objected, "what about the question of price you were talking about earlier? And wouldn't you agree that because women tend to live their lives through men, a woman will complain about her husband when her real complaint is against the terms on which women live their lives? And that's not the man's fault. He didn't make the terms. As Vingtot says, the personal tragedy that Berenice faces is not that her husband is unlike other men, but that he's just the same as other men, all of us bluebottles."

Mary intervened: "Nancy," she said quietly, "you were saying before, that people give up their marriages too easily, that the home should come first and that people should endure, that in particular women should endure. But now because John has

150

become a successful business-man and his wife only wants to live simply, you say their marriage is at an end. Don't you think your views on endurance could be passed on to your friend Berenice?"

The two women looked at each other for a moment and then Nancy smiled.

To get them away from each other, I said: "Nancy don't you see how your story illustrates my point. This story happens over and over again. But it's too subtle a situation to present to the Divorce Court. It may be that Berenice suffers more than the woman whose husband gives her a bloody nose. But the bloody nose wins. John will get his divorce in three years because of her desertion or at any time they like with a good honest adultery. The Courts know where they are with fornication. It's a sin which everyone knows about. It's what is expected of people. But she'd only embarrass us all if she presented a petition for the death of an illusion."

And then Vingtot spoke the last word: "But she does not wish a divorce at all. She wishes someone to wave a magic wand."

And as I was silently adding my private Amen, he shrugged and said to us: "Tout passe, tout casse, tout lasse." But he spoilt the effect by saying a moment later:

"How do you say 'lasse' in English?"

Before Vingtot went to bed he said: "Perhaps you and I could have dinner tomorrow evening?"

I thought of Willie Vincent: "I'd like that very much Vingtot, but I've got an engagement after dinner."

"That will be O.K.," he said, practising his idiom, "what I have to say will not be long," and then he fell over a lamp which fortunately broke and he was able to show off his most apologetic phrases.

I helped Mary carry the plates into the kitchen. "Shall we wash up now or is Henriette coming in the morning?" I asked.

"Let's do it now," she said. "It'll only take a minute." It took us ten minutes and most of them were silent. Then she said: "Do you think Nancy's right that people don't try hard enough to make marriage work?"

I thought for a moment. "Yes I think she is right," I said.

Mary said nothing and for a little while she handed me things to dry.

"Well, what more could we have done?" she asked.

I don't know why I hadn't seen where this conversation might be leading, but I hadn't. I thought to myself wearily that there was nowhere on the face of the earth where a man might take off his shell to rest for a moment. And I simply couldn't cope any more tonight, so I said anything that came out of my mouth, anything to end the conversation.

"I don't know."

"We just don't get on, do we?" she said. But I didn't know whether this was really a question or rather an answer.

"I don't know Mary."

She looked at me, holding a cup in her hand.

"You don't seem very interested," she said drily.

I feverishly searched for friendly words which would show my interest and also end the conversation. I felt dissociated, a state of being which was incommunicable, in which I made enemies and lost friends, which I had early tried to reckon with and yet even now could do nothing about. I had tried to explain this state to Mary as I had tried to explain to my friends, without much success. Everyone, I had argued, is entitled occasionally to let go the reins, though this was not the parallel. The truth was that the reins had let go of me, but how can you say this to anybody? So I had insisted that a man must from time to time disengage, and be the idle singer of an empty day. But these things require at least the acquiescence of the people to whom one is engaged. And it was withheld, except for Willie Vincent. Only he gave me leave. Everybody else said that no one could claim irresponsibility for words and actions—not even temporarily, unless he were mad. So I couldn't say to Mary that I was incapable of answering, and if I didn't answer I should be rude.

"Of course I'm interested," I said speaking slowly. By speaking slowly I could force myself to listen to what I was saying, and if I went wrong I could break in and try and put it right. "But tonight I simply don't know whether we get on or not." Then I said hopefully: "Perhaps we could discuss it tomorrow."

Another mistake. I had slipped unwittingly into our familiar way of insulting each other. Or perhaps it wasn't so unwitting.

She turned back to the cup in her hand. As she handed it to me to dry, I saw that her face was wet. I had the most terrible urge to laugh. I could feel my belly rumbling with the effort to keep it down. I didn't want to laugh at Mary because she was crying, but at me because I wasn't. But mostly I wanted to laugh at the grotesque state in which the Lords of Creation find themselves. On Tuesday evening if Mary had wept, we might have come together again, because I had felt like it. But she hadn't wept and so we had remained divided. This evening she was weeping, and if I had been able to weep, again we might have made something together. But this evening I didn't feel like it and so we would remain apart. Really the whole thing was cosmically comic. And what made it worse was that I wasn't even allowed to laugh.

And then the washing-up was done. Mary went to bed and I let her go without a restraining word. As I mooched up and down the kitchen waiting for her to fall asleep, my mood began to change and as it fell from me, I began for the first time to become suspicious of myself. Perhaps it was I who didn't really want to be reconciled. Otherwise how could I explain the last few minutes? A friendly word, a kiss, a little warmth, even a little interest, and we might have made a new start. But I had been locked up, unapproachable. It was altogether quite remarkable I thought how little I knew about myself, how little I was in control of myself, and most disconcerting of all, how little knowledge I had of my own means of betraying myself.

And then I went to bed.

FRIDAY

There was a letter from Diggins lying on top of the correspondence on my desk. I felt a curious twinge as I recognised the handwriting. The letter was addressed to me personally, so it hadn't been opened with the rest of the post. I opened it slowly and speculatively. I didn't know quite what I expected, but it seemed somehow to be important. It was an oddly formal letter, the kind you write when you are choosing your words carefully or when someone is looking over your shoulder as you're writing. I was pretty sure his wife didn't look over his shoulder so it must have been Diggins himself looking over his own shoulder.

Thursday.

Dear Mr. Mortlock,

I am very glad to be able to let you know that my wife and I are now reconciled and she will be coming back to Australia with the children and me as soon as we get the Court Order rescinded. She is instructing her solicitors to do what is necessary and I hope you will assist as far as you can.

I shall stay with my wife at her parents' home until the formalities are over.

It is difficult for me to put into words my appreciation of your help. At our interview on Tuesday I found your advice strange, but I acted on it and it turned out to be right.

Yours sincerely,

Ezra Diggins.

Ezra, I thought, I should have remembered that. That fundamentalist background might have given me a clue. But what would I have done with a clue? What was it a clue to? And anyway the totality of the man had prevented the isolation of single and individual characteristics. As I held his letter in my hand, I felt neither pleasure at his success nor hurt by my own failure. I was slightly surprised that he didn't say he would come and see me. I should like to have known what had happened. But I dare say he was busy consolidating; he had given enough away when we'd last met. I felt vaguely sorry for his wife, but that wasn't my affair. He wanted her back and he'd got her back. It wasn't going to be any worse for her than it was for a lot of other people. And who knows what goes on between a man and a woman, when more often than not they don't know themselves?

But I didn't feel very comfortable even now when I thought of the advice I had given him on Tuesday. It had been presumptuous; that it had succeeded reflected no credit on me.

Then the telephone began to ring and by the time I had been through the post, I was a long way away from Diggins. The papers had come back from Counsel in the Jones case rather more quickly than usual. As I looked at the draft Petition and read the dry wizened words, they seemed hardly to belong to the turbulent story which Henry had told me of the lives and loves of the Jones family. Even the names, Henry Jones, Helena Jones, Patrick Smith, appeared like ciphers. I checked the formalities and then flipped over the page:

9. That the Respondent has since the celebration of the said marriage committed adultery with one Patrick Smith (hereinafter called "the Co-Respondent").

10. That between June 1951 and the 21st day of November 1953 the Respondent and the Co-Respondent lived and cohabited and habitually committed adultery at 66 Morgan Mews aforesaid.

11. That on the 21st day of November 1953 the Respondent deserted the Petitioner in that on the said date the Petitioner with the knowledge of the Respondent's said adultery invited her to resume cohabitation with him whereupon the Respondent refused to do so and left the said premises with the Co-Respondent and has ever since without cause or the consent of the Petitioner lived separate and apart from him.

12. That since the matters alleged in paragraph 11 hereof the Respondent and the Co-Respondent have lived and cohabited and habitually committed adultery at 1699 High Road, Finsley in the County of Becks where they are still living and cohabiting.

13. That the Petitioner condoned the adultery alleged in paragraph 10 hereof but that the said acts of adultery were revived by the facts alleged in paragraphs 11 and 12 hereof.

And that was about all. The history of Jones' little episode with his wife's sister would be contained in his discretion statement which would be lodged at the Court in a sealed envelope, to be read by the Judge at the trial. Nothing about that was mentioned in the body of the Petition. Anybody reading the Petition who didn't know where to look or what to look for, would have thought Jones was a model of purity and tolerance. Only one small sentence in the Prayer gave him away:

THE PETITIONER THEREFORE PRAYS:
1. That the discretion of the Court be exercised in his favour.
2. That his said marriage may be dissolved.
3. That the Co-Respondent may be ordered to pay the costs of this suit.
4. That the Petitioner may have such further or other relief as may be just.

Asking for the Court's discretion didn't mean that you had a secret you wanted to whisper discreetly to the Judge when nobody was listening. It didn't mean that you wanted forgiveness because you had smelly breath or dirty habits. It meant that you had committed adultery. And in an undefended case only the Judge was to know about it and if you were polite and said you were sorry, he would almost certainly exercise his discretion and forgive you. You can do pretty well anything you like in England if only you say you're sorry. But even after all these years it still seemed to me a curious word to use.

While I was in the middle of the Arbitration file trying to sort out the claims and counterclaims, the telephone rang. It was Henry telephoning from the Court. He had been watching Charbles v. Charbles. He said: "We're on in Divorce Court 6 and we're three out."

"Right. I'll leave now. Hang on till I come." I looked at my watch making the automatic deduction. It had just gone twelve. The case would be on in about half an hour and I flew out of the office into a taxi with most of my mind still inside the Arbitration. I had just about wrenched myself clear of it by the time I got to the Divorce Court. I looked at the list of undefended cases outside Court 6. The Usher was crossing off the case which had just been heard. Nine cases had been crossed off. Now they were hearing number ten and Charbles *v.* Charbles was number eleven. We were acting for the Petitioner, Dr. Charbles.

Hopman came over. Hopman was a Solicitor and a fairly close friend of mine. He knew both Victor Charbles and Evelyn Charbles and when trouble broke out between them, he preferred not to act and passed Victor over to me. As it turned out, it was just as well because he was going to give evidence on Victor's behalf.

"Thank God you've come," he said. "I thought you'd forgotten."

"My Managing Clerk's here. Haven't you seen him?"

"No, I haven't." He seemed nervous. Hopman had a considerable divorce practice and must have acted professionally in hundreds of divorces, but I suppose that doesn't stop you being nervous when you're a witness yourself. I hardly liked to repeat the patter I usually handed out to a witness, but it's always a good thing to go into Court and get used to the atmosphere before you give evidence yourself. So I steered him into Court and sat him next to me behind Counsel.

We bowed to the Judge. It was a County Court Judge called Biggles. He had been brought into the Divorce Court temporarily to help out and was sitting as a Special Commissioner. I had once appeared before him in his County Court years ago. All I remembered of him then was that he had spent the larger part of the day picking his nose. He wasn't picking his nose today, but then today he was in the High Court.

"What's this chap like?" I whispered to Henry.

"Pretty good," he answered. This meant that he wasn't causing any trouble, that he was granting decrees as asked.

Henry said: "I'll slip back to the office now."

"All right Henry. Thank you for watching."

It was important to be in Court from the time the Court sat at ten-thirty. You could never be quite sure how long each case would last and some cases might be transferred to another Judge. Anything might happen and someone always had to be there.

157

It was the best possible way of wasting everybody's time except the Judge's, but it was only the Judges who publicly complained of time being wasted.

Then Biggles said in a rather bored voice, though it probably sounded pretty good to the Petitioner: "Very well. Decree Nisi and costs against the Respondent."

I looked at my watch. After deducting twenty minutes, it was twenty-five minutes past twelve. The end of ten marriages in an hour and fifty-five minutes. It was all very business-like no doubt, but how else could a Court deal with broken marriages except like this, coldly and I always thought rather brutally. And however much you might prefer marriages to be dissolved by other means than this unsatisfactory judicial process, I couldn't myself see how it would advantage either party. But still it was pretty sickening. Ten marriages ended in a hundred and fifteen minutes. And when you thought how those twenty people had started out and how they had finished up . . . The Associate sitting below the Judge, called out the next case: "Charbles v. Charbles."

Counsel got up from the row in front of Hopman and me and said: "May it please your Lordship, this is a husband's Petition for divorce on the ground of desertion. This is a discretion case My Lord."

Although a County Court Judge when in his own Court is addressed as "Your Honour" while sitting as a Special Commissioner he holds the acting rank of High Court Judge and is entitled to the stripes of the rank. In this case the stripes are the titles of "My Lord" and "Your Lordship". As I looked at Biggles apparently paying no attention to the deferential mode of address, I thought how hard it must be for Judges to remain normal after being My Lorded and Your Lordshipped all day. Does a Judge, can a Judge go straight from majesty to mowing a lawn like the rest of us? How can a Judge put up with his wife's nagging when he remembers he was called "My Lord", a hundred and fifty-five times before he got home? I should think it must be rather hard being a Judge. What could you say when in a particularly difficult domestic situation you were told, "You're not in your silly Court now and no one's going to give you those ridiculous titles here. You'll eat what's on the table and like it. There's nothing else left in the house." Yes, it were better far not to be a Judge.

Counsel was a man of my own age called Newing. He had been called to the Bar at about the same time as Hopman and I had been admitted as solicitors. Hopman and I had been lucky. We were both partners and we each earned about £2,000 a year, which is better than the average for a London Solicitor. Newing had been unlucky. He was in a bad set of chambers and I doubt if he earned £750 a year. As a barrister if you get into a good set of chambers, you have the best possible start with the crumbs that fall from the tables of the busy men in chambers. But good chambers are few, and bad chambers many. And if you start in bad chambers you have a hard fight unless you know solicitors who will give you work.

Hopman and I had introduced Newing to a number of solicitors but he didn't get much work just the same. I suppose the reason why they didn't send him work was the reason why I didn't and Hopman didn't. And the reason was his inexperience. I know that people learn by mistakes and that everybody has to start somewhere, but I couldn't see why anyone should learn at the expense of my clients. And I dare say the other solicitors felt the same. All the simpler work I got, I parcelled out between Newing and half a dozen other people like him. But a good deal of my work was complicated, requiring specialist handling and I couldn't afford to trust it to people like Newing. I was sorry about it and wished I could do more, but the interests of the clients always had to come first. And anyway the system which divided the legal profession in half seemed to me out of date. Either the professions should be fused or something should be done to put an end to the dreary social waste at the Bar. Too many young barristers seemed to spend their time drinking coffee or gossiping in Chambers because they had no work, while too many solicitors drafted documents in trains and read papers in bed because they had too much.

Newing was saying: "Dr. Charbles please," and Victor Charbles went into the witness-box and took the oath.

It all went smoothly until Newing asked:

"Dr. Charbles, will you tell My Lord what happened on the 14th January 1954?"

For the first time Victor Charbles lost his composure. He had, up to this point, been doing very well. He was answering shortly, speaking clearly, with his head turned towards the Judge, everything according to the book. But now he passed his hand over his brow, a short sturdy little man with a fine head and good bones in his face, wondering how to compress into a few words, the events of an evening which would live as long as he did. At last he said in a thick muffled voice:

"We had a dreadful scene. My wife told me that she hated me and never wanted to see me again." Then he came to a full stop.

Newing coughed sympathetically in order to cover a pause during which Victor Charbles' distress might become apparent to the Judge. But whether it did or no, Biggles' face didn't move from his pen. That pen had been moving over paper throughout the case, but whether it was making notes or drawing faces it was impossible to tell.

Newing said quietly: "And then?"

"She packed a bag, woke the boy and they both left the house." He added as an afterthought: "She also took the dog."

Charbles and I had had some trouble over this, because he wanted the dog back. I had told him that you can't get custody of a dog and that a husband cannot sue his wife in tort, but I had had a dreadful job to prevent him starting proceedings over the dog. People are odd. He'd raised no objection to his wife having the child whom no doubt he loved more than the dog, but he'd been prepared to go to quite extraordinary lengths to get that dog back.

Newing ignored the afterthought and went on stolidly:

"Did you know where she was going?"

"Oh yes, she told me. She went to the house of friends, Mr. and Mrs. Hopman in Watford."

I felt Hopman wince. He was remembering how Evelyn Charbles had arrived at his sleeping home unannounced at half-past two in the morning.

The vital part of the evidence was now over and Newing tied up the loose ends.

The Law regards the spouse who is successfully sued for divorce as the guilty party. In this case, if we were successful Evelyn Charbles would be the guilty wife. But it seemed to me that in almost every divorce, both parties were at the same time guilty and not guilty. They were both guilty in the sense that each had contributed to the breakdown of the marriage. It takes two people to maintain or destroy a marriage, though I agreed with Nancy Andrews that the responsibility on the woman is higher, if only because she usually has more at stake. And they were not guilty in the sense that whatever they did or didn't do, usually neither deliberately intended to break up the home. Anyway the word guilt in divorce is largely meaningless. What really happens between two people which finally brings them before the Court, is something that the Court never knows. But the importance to a husband of establishing guilt in the wife is that a guilty wife forfeits her Common Law right to be maintained, though the Court has by statute a discretion to grant it. This didn't apply in our case. Victor Charbles had been maintaining his wife ever since she had left him and he intended to go on maintaining her.

Newing shuffled among the papers in front of him and handed the acknowledgement of service of the Petition to the Usher who gave it to the witness.

"Do you recognise the signature at the foot of that document?" Newing asked.

"Yes, it's my wife's."

That proved the service of the Petition. The last thing was Victor's adultery.

Newing said: "Please let the witness see his discretion statement."

Victor Charbles looked at the piece of paper handed to him by the Usher.

"Do you recognise the signature at the foot of that document?"

"Yes, it's mine."

"Did you read the document before you signed it?"

"Yes."

"Does that document accurately set out the particulars of your adultery?"

"It does."

"Have you committed adultery with any other person or in any other circumstances except as mentioned in that document?"

"No, I have not."

Now it was almost over. As an example of an undefended divorce, it was a fair specimen. And as always, every element of passion, of the emotion that had ever stirred two people had been squeezed out. So although it was interesting to prepare an undefended divorce suit, it was boring to listen to. I listened only with my professional ear, to make sure that everything was working according to plan, ticking off every item as it was passed. All my other ears were closed and this was another reason why I was glad to be a solicitor rather than a barrister who largely handled pieces of paper and the formalities of evidence. It was the solicitor who had the interesting job of arranging the people in the pack. The barrister merely dealt the cards.

Newing said: "Thank you Dr. Charbles. Mr. Hopman please."

Hopman crowded past the solicitors and clerks waiting for their cases and went into the box. As he took the oath, I gestured to Victor Charbles to come and sit next to me. He squeezed past the same people to take Hopman's place. I said in a whisper: "You did very well," but he only nodded. In about two minutes he would be divorced and it was clear from his face that he wasn't altogether happy about it. I had thought that he had become reconciled to his new life and had decided to start again with someone else. Perhaps he also thought he had, but now I could see that before he made his decision he must have carefully excluded from his mind all the apparatus that was still joined to his wife, so that he could make a decision relying upon evidence that leaned all one way. And it wasn't simply that his decision had been based on insufficient evidence. All decisions are made on insufficient evidence. But the evidence he had used had been partial. I could understand this very well. Everyone I knew, including me, behaved in exactly the same way. I dare say it wasn't done consciously or knowingly, but the result was exactly the same. So we all made the decisions involving our emotional lives having picked only the evidence which pointed in the particular direction we thought we wanted to go. And then one day all the things we'd carefully left out turned up. And we knew that the much considered, wisely pondered decision was wrong. This was happening today to Victor Charbles in the Divorce Court.

Newing was saying, "Is your full name Anthony Verdun Hopman?"

"It is."

Biggles looked up:

"We all know where your father was when your mother was in a certain condition," he smirked.

A roar of obsequious laughter went round the Court. Newing laughed the loudest and I thought for one moment that he was never going to stop. But eventually he did and took Hopman through his evidence, that Evelyn Charbles with her child had arrived at his home in the early hours of the 15th January 1954, that he had tried unsuccessfully to persuade her to return to her husband and the subsequent history. Newing's last question was:

"From what you know of the circumstances, Mr. Hopman would you say that Dr. Charbles has tried to get his wife back in every way possible?"

"I would. No man could have tried harder."

"Thank you Mr. Hopman. My Lord, I have a further witness who can prove that the Petitioner has lived separate and apart from his wife since the 14th January 1954. But in view of Mr. Hopman's evidence my Lord, you may feel that I need not take up the time of the Court." We all waited. The witness was Victor's housekeeper and girl friend and we didn't particularly want her to give evidence.

The Judge said in a friendly tone: "No, I don't think you need any more evidence Mr. Newing."

And so Newing in his grandest voice made his supplication. "My Lord, upon the evidence I would ask your Lordship to say that this is a case where Your Lordship could properly exercise your Lordship's discretion in the Petitioner's favour and in the exercise of that discretion and if your Lordship is satisfied with the evidence, I would ask your Lordship to grant the Petitioner a Decree Nisi."

One "My Lord" and five "Your Lordships". That was surely worth a Decree.

Biggles said: "Very well. I find this a proper case in which I may exercise my discretion in the Petitioner's favour. I do so. There will be a Decree Nisi."

And that was that. The Associate called the next case. Despite all the trappings of the Court, I thought as we came out of the door, how undignified it was to dissolve marriages like this. In a way, it would have been more appropriate to have divorces heard in a butcher's shop as the Scotch beef was being carved or the chickens cleaned. At least there would have been symbolism. Blood would have flowed, guts would have been removed; the atmosphere would have been heavy and sacrificial. Blood, guts and sacrifice would have been in harmony with the progress of the marriage until its final destruction in the butcher's shop. Even the sawdust on the floor and the dogs piddling in the doorway would have been fitter accompaniment to the ending of a marriage than the starchy voices of the lawyers as they handed bits of paper round the Court.

I looked at the clock. Not quite a quarter to one. It had taken a bit longer than the average but still, eleven divorces in two and a quarter hours was fast work. I doubted whether the butchers could work faster. But if marriages are made in Heaven, the Divorce Court must have some strange connections.

Victor Charbles was still looking bleak. He'd been married fifteen years and unmarried in just over fifteen minutes. I dare say it takes a bit of getting used to.

"Want some lunch Victor?" I asked, "or would you rather go back to your surgery?"

"Let's have lunch Bill," he said eagerly. I didn't fancy that eagerness much, so I pressed Hopman to come too. Newing came out of Court and handed me his brief already endorsed with the result. It read proudly: "Cor. H.H. Judge Biggles. D.N. L.L. Newing."

Victor asked him to lunch. Newing said: "Let's eat in the crypt."

"No fear," Hopman answered hurriedly. "Let's get away from this place. I don't want to meet any more lawyers. They'll only tell us about their cases. Don't you have enough of it?" And then realising that Newing didn't have enough of it, he said quickly: "If you haven't, then I have. And I've got more bloody cases lying in wait for me the moment I stick my nose inside my office. Come on." And he led us to the Cheshire Cheese where sandwiched between several Americans and various brands of continentals, he told us about his cases.

At two o'clock I'd had enough of Hopman's cases and called the waiter. Hopman snatched the bill away from me. I didn't object. I felt I'd earned my lunch. While he was waiting for his change, he said gloomily to Charbles:

"I don't know why I do anything for you bastards. You never do anything for me. It's pretty nearly impossible to get any of you people to give evidence against another doctor. And if any of your fraternity makes a mistake, he never admits it. I don't know why not," and he humped over the table. Charbles became guarded at once: "My profession's very vulnerable," he said.

"So's mine," Hopman replied sourly. "And yet solicitors are sued for negligence as often as may be. But I'm hanged if you people are. And I don't understand why you all object so much. You're all insured up to the gizzard."

"The reason is that an allegation of negligence is so damaging professionally. You can't blame a young doctor wanting to avoid trouble," Charbles returned.

"I don't blame him for that," Hopman said glowering, "but let one of your profession make a mistake and all the others gather round until the body's been carried away. And then they deny there ever was a body. And you all want to be given an immunity from the consequences of your negligent acts that no other member of the community either has or would have the cheek to ask for."

"There have been a good many actions for negligence against hospitals and doctors since the Legal Aid scheme started," Charbles said defensively.

"I know there have," Hopman replied "and I expect that most of them have been lost because no one could get proper evidence from the doctors. And don't your people get steamed up, now that actions are being brought against them?"

"They don't get steamed up," said Charbles who was by now himself steaming up, "but they don't think it's fair, any more than I do, that doctors should be penalised for their mistakes. They have to learn by experience and experience includes making mistakes."

Hopman moved in again: "I don't want to penalise anybody," he said angrily. "But if a man's negligent, he must face the consequences, whether he's a doctor or a sauerkraut manu-facturer."

"But accidents can happen to the best, most conscientious doctors," Charbles retorted. "And even Homer nodded. Don't you ever nod?"

"Let's leave Homer out of it," Hopman replied fiercely. "And I wasn't talking about accidents. No one's liable for an accident if it really is an accident. I was speaking of negligent mistakes, not accidental mistakes. The trouble is that you chaps don't live up to the standards which your Hippocratic oath lays down for you."

Charbles was red in the face: "Why you swine," he roared, "it's because of you and your kind that we're always looking over our shoulder to see that one of you isn't watching. We're in such a state now that the first thing we think of is whether we can be sued instead of doing what's right for the patient. I don't know how those chaps in the casualty department manage. I'd be terrified myself; I'd always be waiting for a Writ to be served on me. Why do you know," he said turning to Newing and me for support, "that we even have people X-rayed, not because we believe they've got any bones broken but just in case some sharp lawyer tries to catch us out later?" He spread his hands. "Really, how do you think this kind of persecution does anybody any good, least of all the patient?"

I suspected that Hopman had perhaps only started the argument to keep Charbles' mind away from the divorce, but he'd succeeded altogether too well. As we trooped into Fleet Street, I said, "You're very grumpy today Hopman. What's up?"

"Nothing specially," he said genially, "except that I'm bowed down by work." And then he began to laugh. "I bought a tape-recorder some months ago to amuse the family. Do you know what I do with it now?"

"No, what?"

"Well, all the files I can't get through during the day, I take home and I dictate letters and memoranda when I'm in bed."

"Wouldn't it be more amusing to take your secretary home and dictate to her in bed?" I asked.

He grinned faintly: "That's what my wife says, but she doesn't think it's a joke. She's always complaining that I never have any time for her and the children. Doesn't Mary ever complain?"

I was taken aback. "Mary?" I said involuntarily. "Oh no, she never complains."

And then I went back to my office.

AFTERNOON

Anne said: "Mr. Green has telephoned four times. He says his wife rings him up and threatens to commit suicide unless he goes back to live with her. He wants to know what to do."

"How should I know?" I asked, leaning back in my chair and looking at her. I wondered how she managed to look so young and stay so fresh in our private graveyard.

"Well he asked if you'd ring the moment you came in."

"All right," I said. "Ring him."

When the call came through, I came straight to the point: "Do you want to go back to your wife, Mr. Green?"

There was a long pause.

"If I don't," he said at last in a hollow voice, "she says she'll commit suicide."

"Yes I know about that. But do you want to go back?"

There was another long pause. Finally he said, "No." He didn't sound very sure. But we'd soon find out.

"Very well," I said, "let her."

"Let her what?" he asked.

"Let her commit suicide."

Enough time elapsed for him to have committed suicide himself before he answered.

"I can't do that," he said at last.

"Why can't you?"

"Because I can't." His voice was surer now. At least there was one thing he could make up his mind about.

"Then you'll have to go back, won't you?" I said.

"But I don't want to," he said complainingly.

There were some people whose weakness I was prepared to subsidise, but this man wasn't one of them. It was this man's weakness which I was pretty sure had ruined his marriage. His wife had trodden all over him and when she found he didn't object, she did it all the more. It's a mistake to lie down under somebody else's heel. The impulse of all mankind is to grind it in.

This man had to learn to get up. It wasn't my job to teach him.

He needed a psychiatrist like so many other people I acted for. But they wouldn't go so I had to do the best I could. Always I got these weak little men, constitutionally incapable of making up their minds. Why? More and more rarely I got normal men and women who fell out of love with each other and fell in love with other people. That's a good reason for divorce. Something constructive could come out of that. But mostly these people didn't come to me. Now I only got people whose marriages were unhappy, who wanted and who didn't want to be divorced, who loved and hated their wives and who didn't or couldn't love anybody else. Perhaps, I thought, it was I who needed the psychiatrist and not so much they. What was it that these people needed which they thought I could give them?

I could see that I would tend more and more to have a practice consisting of my own kind. My clients were sent to me by my friends. My friends were generally my own kind of person. Their friends who became my clients would tend to be the same. So far I could see. But what I couldn't see was, why did these people almost always come about divorce and why did they almost always want not a divorce, but a magical rebirth.

"Mr. Green," I said firmly. "You had in my opinion every reason to leave your wife. As you know I think you should have thrown her out ages ago when she taunted you with her adultery. You wouldn't throw her out and chose to leave yourself. And here you are, you haven't been gone a month and you're not sure what to do when she makes a threat. But," I said warningly, "if you give in now, you'll be at her mercy for the rest of your life. Think this over carefully. I know you don't really want a divorce. I know you want to be happily married all over again with the past blotted out. You may even later come to terms with your wife. But not now. Not because she makes a threat."

I stopped, sickened with myself. I'd done it again. Why couldn't I mind my own business? A small frightened voice said: "Yes, I know, but this threat is suicide."

"What other threat could she make?" I snarled, angry with myself rather than him. I had heard too many threats of suicide to take them seriously. If people were really bent on taking their own lives, they took them. They didn't tell you first. He would have to take a chance, if it was a chance; it was his own fault that he'd allowed this situation to arise.

"You really think I shouldn't go back?" he quavered.

"That's for you to say, Mr. Green." Only toughness would force him to face the issue, if anything would. "I can't decide that for you."

"All right," he said in a hopeless voice and rang off. And I knew that she'd won. She had frightened him and he was going back. I was angry at first, but then I gave up. What did it matter? She needed someone to eat and he needed someone to eat him. They'd got the taste for each other. They might just as well stay together.

I couldn't face any more divorce and I looked over to the corner of the table on which I had stacked the new files which still had to be read. I took the top one and began to read it. We acted for an English Company which had bought goods from an unpronounceable West German firm and sold them to an unpronounceable Norwegian firm. The German firm had defaulted and the Norwegian firm was complaining. It looked as if the English Company had two actions on its hands, one by the Norwegians and one against the Germans. The easiest way out would have been for the Norwegians to have sued the Germans, but this couldn't be done because the Norwegians hadn't directly contracted with the Germans. The Norwegians would have to sue us and we would have to sue the Germans. Matters were made worse because the German firm was not strong financially and an action against them might be a waste of money. It looked as if the best course would be to see whether the contract with the Norwegian firm could be upset and if not, to settle on the best terms we could get. I began to make detailed notes until I discovered that the contract with the Norwegians didn't specify what Law governed the contract. It could be English Law or Norwegian Law perhaps even German Law and I had to look up the books. I cursed the clients. I had told them a dozen times that if they wanted to save confusion and expense they should say specifically in any contracts they made with foreigners that English Law governed. After a good deal of searching and puffing and blowing, I came to the conclusion that English Law governed which was a relief because it meant there was some chance of me knowing what I was talking about.

But it took a long time, during which the post came in and went out signed and everybody went home.

"Well," I said to Vingtot as we were eating, "what did Professor Pumper teach you today?"

"The English 'o'," he said seriously. The pronunciation was so English that it sounded wrong coming from Vingtot and I exploded with mirth.

"Really Vingtot," I complained, "you'll be the death of me."

Eagerly he looked across the table: "The death ... of ... me," he intoned. He produced a huge black notebook and wrote furiously. "Now," he said, looking up very pleased, "The ... death ... of ... me—what is that?"

He didn't get to the point until I said I had to leave. Then he looked distressed and spread his hands.

"Oh my dear friend," he said, "what is the matter in your house?"

I told him.

"But you cannot continue to live like that," he said.

"What's the alternative?"

"You must leave," he said gravely.

I told him about Susan, but he shook his head:

"No, no, you should not stay. I could smell the unhappiness there. It is not good." And he wrinkled his nose to illustrate the point.

"But surely," I said, "it's better for the children as it is?"

He shook his head again. "Sometimes, yes," he replied slowly. "But not here. It will be better for everybody if you go."

I didn't want to hear any more so I stood up to go. There was no need for me to see him back to his hostel. It was in the same street as the restaurant. He looked at me sadly and started to speak, but I shook his hand and rushed off without waiting to hear it.

EVENING

A woman I'd never seen before let me in. She looked vaguely Scandinavian.

"Hello Willie," I said. Willie Vincent got out of an armchair. He was wearing wide red cloth braces over a grey shirt.

"Hello Bill, have a drink."

While he was pouring the beer, he said:

"Any murders lately?"

"No, no murders."

"I hear you rang on Tuesday. Anything special?"

"No, nothing special."

"Fifi said you sounded demented."

"Who's Fifi?"

He jerked his chin towards the window and there sitting in a seat with her feet curled up was the girl who had let me in. I stared at her for a moment. She had a peaky elfin face.

"How do you do?" I said.

She bowed her head. It was the colour Van Gogh uses to exaggerate a cornfield.

"She can't speak English," Willie said.

"How can her name be Fifi?" I asked. We were talking as if she weren't there.

"I can't pronounce her name and I thought she looked like a kitten," he said.

"How can you have a yellow kitten?"

"Don't argue Bill. Just drink your beer."

Then it occurred to me that the woman I'd spoken to on Tuesday spoke English very well.

"How could Fifi know I sounded demented if she can't speak English?"

"That was her sister who spoke to you on the 'phone."

This was the kind of inconsequential conversation which I was always having with Willie. I never knew at the time whether I liked it or not.

"How did you get her, Willie?"

"She came over here three weeks ago to live with a family and look after the children." Then he said:

"She wants to learn English," as if he were surprised.

"Well what happened to the family?"

"Apparently the man made a pass at her so she complained to her sister. And I knew her sister. That's all."

"What's the difference between a paterfamilias making a pass at her and you making a pass at her?" I asked.

He shrugged. "It's nicer for me."

I couldn't make all this out. It seemed an unlikely enough story but I wasn't in my office and it didn't really matter whether it made sense or not. Just the same I felt slightly nettled.

He put his hands through his braces and stretched his feet out. He looked as if he were making himself comfortable but also as if he were preparing an assault.

"Fifi," he said loudly, looking towards the girl, "go to bed." She got up on the instant and left the room, bowing to me as she went.

"I thought you said she didn't understand English."

"Oh she understands what I say," he replied.

Then he lay back in his chair, a bulky solid person and scratched his chest. He was indicating that he was ready to be talked to. I had ached to talk to him on Tuesday, but now I couldn't find anything to say.

"How's Mary?" he asked with an indifferent air.

"She's all right."

"And the children?"

"And the children."

And then neither of us said anything. I didn't want to tell him about Mary. I tried twice and the words stuck in my throat. So I just sat there. I looked round the room. Everything appeared to be as usual except that over his desk there was a new frame. I got up and looked at it. It was a quotation: "C'est bien plus beau lorsque c'est inutile." I spelled out the translation to myself slowly:

"And it's all the better for being useless."

"Rostand's Cyrano de Bergerac," Willie said. "I think it's rather appropriate to describe how I live, don't you?"

"No I don't," I replied. "You don't live on that principle."

He laughed. "Yes I do," he said. "You don't think I do

because you don't." He laughed again: "You know Bill, some-times you remind me of one of those earnest adolescents with great big hungry eyes looking at the world as if it were a magic place. How is it you never learn, particularly in your job?" Then he leaned forward. "Has it never occurred to you why all these lame ducks come to consult you, all these people you tell me about who can't make up their own minds?"

I was a bit frightened. How could he know what had been drumming in my head all the week?

I lied. "No," I said, "it hasn't. You tell me why they come."

"Because you're a great big universal mother," he replied, "that's why. You've told me yourself that you're rarely consulted by unhappy women, but mostly by unhappy men and from the stories you've told me and the ones I can guess, it's pretty clear that they come to you for protection. The product of dominating mothers, married to dominating wives, they've had all their masculinity nearly knocked out of them. So they turn to you. And why do you think they turn to you?" He paused for my reply. I had the feeling that he was playing me, taking me step by step to a place I didn't want to go, just as I did myself to other people in my office. I didn't like it much.

"Well, why?"

"Because they're involved in a homosexual relationship with you. Have you never felt it? When these poor creatures come to you, castrated first by mother and then by wife, do you not feel the insistent urge from them? They don't come to you because you're a good lawyer Bill, though for all I know, you may be. They come to you because you're going to love them, because you're going to make it all right for them. You're going to tuck them up like a good mother does, the good mother they never had. And then when they're tucked up nicely and they feel warm and safe, you're going to say to them: 'Now, you just leave it all to me. I'll make it better for you.' And you're also going to love them like their wives ought to but don't. You don't have to get into bed with them you know Bill," he said with a grin, after looking at my face, "they'll be content with less than that."

So this was one of the answers, was it? I remembered the momentary glimmer I had had while I had been talking to Jordan and in the train after seeing Miss Gill. And Willie's words fell into place like pieces of a jigsaw. But I felt as if all the breath had been knocked out of me. I didn't doubt for a moment that what he'd said was right. But how did I come to be in this kind of state?

He went on quickly as if to get it all over at once:

"Anyway Bill," he said, "can't you see that your premise is wrong? You think you're really helping people." He waved his hands and gave a sonorous laugh but it contained no amusement. "You don't help anybody," he said loudly, almost contemptuously, "you can't help anybody. And nor can anyone else. If people are helpable, they can in the last resort manage by themselves. So they don't need you, and let me assure you, it's no kindness to them to clog their lives with a benefactor they can do without. And if they are not helpable, you do them no kindness by offering your assistance. At best you are a crutch. And if you're not prepared to have them hanging round your neck for the rest of your life, don't offer your help. Because later you'll take it away and then they'll be worse off than they were to start with. If they can't be helped, leave them alone and mind your own business."

He looked at me lying limply in my chair and got in another thrust: "Why do you want to be a benefactor anyway?"

I had been asking myself this ever since he'd been talking. But I hadn't found an answer. He got up and poured out some more beer. I was glad of the respite. I couldn't possibly have answered the accusation until I'd had time privately to digest it. As he sat down again, he was grinning:

"You know," he said in a friendly tone, "you're overworking your intuitive faculty on other people. It's a pity you don't train it on yourself. It's time you stopped knowing about other people. Time you started knowing about yourself," and he sat in his chair chuckling.

"Well, what's so funny?" I asked testily.

He burst into laughter. "You," he said. "Old clever dick Mortlock. That's what's funny. I was thinking of that old woman you told me about who was always lending money to people and always getting in a mess. When they didn't pay her back, she never knew whether to sue or not. If she sued and got it back, you said she felt ashamed for having been so nasty and if she sued and didn't get it back, she got angry because she thought

174

she'd been tricked. And if she didn't sue, she was always wondering if she ought. You told me how you'd warned her times out of number not to lend money, but she went on doing it. Eventually you stopped warning her because you saw why she was compelled to lend money. She wanted people to love her and this was the only way she knew how to get their love. She was old of course," he added, and burst into another guffaw.

"Well?" I said coldly.

It was some time before he stopped laughing. Then his face still pink, he pointed a finger at me:

"And what do you think you're doing?"

My mouth was tightly shut but I could feel the muscles at the side of my jaw twitching. I was beginning to think that I couldn't cope with any more revelations, when Willie made it easier for me by changing the subject in his usual roundabout way so that I had hardly time to notice before I was pitched in somewhere else.

"I should think your starting-off point might be different Bill," he said quietly. "That might help you. Suppose you reckoned with the perhaps unpleasant truth that most people haven't got anything to offer, particularly women. I know it's different when you're young but you're over thirty-five now. The balance has swung in your favour."

"What balance?" I asked.

"The balance of advantage between men and women. You think about it for a minute. Wouldn't you say that by and large, a reasonably attractive woman gets the better of it while she's young, say until she's thirty-five, but that about thirty-five the balance swings in favour of men, and swings perhaps rather heavily in their favour?"

I thought about it. "Well," I said slowly, "I'd never thought of it quite like that before. But I see what you mean."

"We were considering women," he continued without listening, "and we were considering them rather unfavourably. Don't think this is pique. It's not. But as I have devoted a large part of my life to pursuing women and plotting to get them into bed, it seems to me a subject worth a bit of thought." He stopped for a moment. "Particularly as I have every intention of continuing to pursue them and of plotting as aforesaid."

He stretched himself more comfortably in his chair: "Now it is some time," he said expansively, "since I have kept a list of the women I've had. I have grown out of that habit, though I believe there are some men who count their tally until the day they die. Weakness of course," he said getting up and going to the table, "a form of whistling in the dark, proof of manhood, like growing a beard. And you realise of course," he said turning towards me, "that the need to prove your manhood only arises when you suspect it."

He poured out some more beer and went back to his chair.

"Now about women," he said easily. "From the vantage-point of near middle age, as I walk through the streets, I observe the girls joggling along, with their little titties waggling, half proud, half anxious. And I feel sad for them." He shook his head mournfully: "I do," he said, full of apparent concern, "I feel sad for them, because when it comes down to it, what have they got to offer but the pleasures of fornication? Not that they're much good at it, most of them," he added gloomily. He fell silent and pondered the sorrow of it all but a moment later he went on thoughtfully:

"Bill, has it never occurred to you what a gross affair making love is?"

"No," I said, sipping my beer. "I'm afraid it hasn't. But in view of your history, this monkish view doesn't become you very well."

"It isn't really monkish you know," he said. "You're thinking of the second-century heresies which eventually contaminated Christian doctrine. But I wasn't thinking of it theologically. It only occurred to me because the other day I was considering the subtler pleasures of the senses, tastes, smells, sights, sounds, feel, and then I came to bodies. And I felt repelled when I thought of all that mountainous, odorous flesh, of the messiness of spasm and secretion. I thought of all that struggling and heaving and it made me feel sick. Haven't you ever felt sick at the thought of it?" he asked suddenly.

"No," I said firmly, "I'm sorry but I can't say I have "

"I have," he continued wryly, "frequently at great cost to myself in time, energy and money, found myself involved in this jungle encounter with a lady. And sometimes while all the roaring was going on, I have found myself wishing that I were miles away, sitting on a five-barred gate in a field, with the green taste of a grass in my mouth. I suppose I prefer the subtler to the

176

grosser, that's all." He shrugged. "Only sometimes of course," he added reflectively, "only at the moment, you might say, of impact. I don't know which I would prefer now." And he smiled and rolled his eyes upwards to where I imagined Fifi was lying in wait for him. "I should have to await the offer which would compel the choice," he said.

And then I suppose he thought I'd had time to recover and could take one last assault, because he moved the subject back. "And talking of what people have to offer, I noticed the other day that your favourite author seems to suffer from the same delusion as you. He also thinks everybody has something to offer. He put it rather well I thought: 'Every creature can impart to some other, his music or his fragrance or his flame.' But I fear you're both wrong. Most people haven't anything to offer, neither music, fragrance, flame or anything else. And I must say I like it better like that. It means I'm not committed."

"Well whatever they've got or haven't got," I grunted, "I certainly don't want them to offer it to me. What's the quotation?"

"Proust."

"You've gone very Gallic."

"I think it's having Fifi around," he replied.

"But Fifi's surely some kind of Scandinavian," I said, puzzled.

"Yes, she's a Swede."

I lay back in my chair. There was no point in pursuing this conversation. It wouldn't lead anywhere. He had fired his bullets and nothing more was going to emerge. I still hadn't recovered from his bullets and not only because they had reached their target but also because they had been fired at all. It was unlike Willie to be so direct. Usually his approach was as oblique as a cat's. But now the discussion would meander vaguely, aimlessly. I said what was in my mind:

"How is it, Willie that a discussion with you never has a shape? I except your views about my role towards the anguish of man, published for the first time this evening. But normally our talks always remain formless; no conclusions ever follow what we say. Why is this?"

He thought for a moment. He was scratching his chest again.

"I suppose," he said hesitantly, "it's because what I say is not only part of a conversation, but is also a commentary, my commentary on affairs."

"Well," I replied, "why should your commentary always be inconclusive?"

"Because life's inconclusive, that's why," he said, snapping his fingers towards the fire as if to encourage a reluctant salamander.

"Is it?" I said, half to myself.

"Really Bill you make me tired. Of course it's inconclusive. There's no beginning and there's no end. It all just goes on, all the time. People get born and die, I know, but these events are just incidental to a process called life and that process grinds on like the machine at the bottom of the sea which goes on grinding salt. Only luckily for me, I shall personally have an end." After a moment he went on: "And yet there are all these bloody fools who want to get involved all over again after they're dead." He laughed mirthlessly and said, "But not me. I'm a genuine isolationist."

"Christ," I said. "What's happened to you?"

He looked up at me, heavily-faced, full-lipped, healthily involved in living, whatever he said.

"You don't really want me to tell you, do you mother mine?"

"No Willie," I replied. "I don't want you to tell me." I was beginning to learn, I thought. I really was beginning to look where I was going.

And then each of us lay back in his chair and we didn't say any more.

"We haven't played chess for a long time," he said at last. "Shall we have a game?"

"Yes," I said gratefully, "let's do that."

And we played chess and drank beer and listened to the Brandenburg concertos and after a time I began to feel civilised again. Perhaps it was because we had stopped talking. I talked too much and listened too much and I was tired of it. What use was talk anyway? The things that were important to me and to everyone else weren't spoken. They were either felt or they weren't felt and no amount of talk helped one way or the other.

At one o'clock I went home. I hoped that Mary would be in. I didn't want to lie awake waiting for her and then have to

pretend to be asleep when she came to bed. So I walked slowly
but still I got to the house in ten minutes. As I walked along the
road, I saw that our bedroom light was on. I went into the kitchen
and made some stewed coffee which took another ten minutes.

I was pretty sure by this time that the bedroom light would be
off. And it was.

A MONTH

AT BREAKFAST Mary said: "I've decided not to go away this week-end, Bill. It's less than a month to Easter and I've arranged to take the children to Mother then."

"All right," I said vaguely. I was wondering where to start first. I could either read the new files which would take a day. Or I could begin on the existing files which I had put aside to think about. They would take about two days. Whichever I did first, the week-end was fully mortgaged.

I worked all Saturday. On Sunday morning we went for a walk. It was a cold bleak day and we walked briskly. The talk was of games at school and gadgets ranging from electric razors to moon rockets. The boys were very superior about their technical knowledge. Michael knew all about radios and electrical circuits and other mysteries of the same kind and he mended all the fuses in the house. Edward was also superior in his field and he was responsible for the interior economy of the house. I wasn't a very handy kind of person and it usually took me a week-end to put in a rawl plug and another week-end to put back the bits of wall I had pulled out. They had taken these matters out of my hands and in my gratitude, I was usually prepared to let them bore me with their talk of technical marvels. But sometimes it got too much for me especially when they began to gabble excitedly about cars. I have never believed the story that people tell how motor cars work, that pistons fly up and down at the speed they say, nor that all the things happen which they say happen. I have tried to believe several times and I tried hardest when they made me do 406 inspections in the Army, but it was no good. I know that cars go because I have seen them go. But so far as I am concerned they go by magic. When I couldn't listen to any more of it I said:

"What happened at school last week?"

Silence.

"Well, what happened?"

"Nothing happened," Michael said in a surly voice.

"Don't be ridiculous," I replied, "a week can't go by with nothing happening."

"Well," said Edward doubtfully, "a boy fell off the railings and twisted his ankle."

"I meant," I explained patiently, "what kind of week did you have? Was it interesting or boring?"

"Boring," they both said without hesitation.

Then I was sorry I had interfered. They'd been so full of life, talking animatedly about what really concerned them and I had spoiled it by bringing back boring old school.

We walked along morosely for a while. Then Edward had an idea: "What sort of a week did you have Daddy?" he asked.

"Oh, all right."

"Interesting or boring?" he asked.

I laughed. "Interesting," I replied.

"What was interesting?"

Silence. What was interesting? What could I say that would be interesting?

"Oh, I don't know," I said at last, "just interesting."

They all laughed. "You see," Michael said reprovingly, "you don't like talking about it either."

The month which followed was much like any other month. People came and went; sometimes they were nice and sometimes they were not. Looking out occasionally from the little box in which I passed my days, I could see that the weather was slowly getting better, but that was about all.

Jordan's case appeared to be turning out well and I was pleased for him. The psychiatrist had seen his wife and sent me a report.

His diagnosis was paranoid schizophrenia.

The report said:

"She told me that she remembered hitting her husband with an iron poker across his shoulders but she thought that she had been justified in doing this because he had kicked one of her friends in the face. I asked her why he had kicked her friend in the face and she said: 'My husband objected to my friends coming through the floor. He always insisted that they should come through the door. That is why he made a scene.' She also admitted that she had repeatedly struck her husband

and that now she was sorry but that he had always deserved whatever she had done because he had plotted with the Devil."

There was a good deal more of this sort of thing, but all that mattered to us was the psychiatrist's opinion that Mrs. Jordan knew what she had been doing at the time and knew it was wrong.

I could see Jordan's tired, grey face as I dictated the letter to him enclosing a copy of the report, so I made the letter cheerful and hopeful, though we were not yet out of the wood. The trial was still six months away and anything might happen between now and then.

It was an unusual pleasure to dictate a letter which was so full of promise. When I'd first been handed the papers certifying Mrs. Jordan and I'd looked at the Reception Order and the Doctor's reports attached to it, the case had seemed hopeless. It is difficult enough at the best of times to succeed on the ground of cruelty, but if the cruel person is mad at the time of the cruelty, it becomes impossible. A mad person isn't cruel, just mad.

Now it was up to Jordan. The psychiatrist had reported that in his opinion Mrs. Jordan was unlikely to recover. Jordan had to make up his mind whether he wanted a divorce, because although his wife was undoubtedly mad, for the purpose of our divorce, she wasn't mad at all.

By the time I had my second interview with Faulkner I had assembled all the information there was to assemble. It wasn't much.

"So far as I can see Harold," I said, "the position appears to be this. You and Reggie contracted to buy machine parts from Browns and they were to deliver them according to sample in six months. When the first batch was delivered, you found they were faulty. You then telephoned Browns to complain and sent them back. Right?"

"Right," he answered.

"Browns presumably did what they thought necessary to the faulty parts and returned them but you decided they were still unfit for your purposes and sent them back. Then it appears that the parts were sent backwards and forwards half a dozen times and now Browns are sick of it and want to be paid. And that's why you're here."

"Right," he repeated.

"But," I said slowly, "the only documents I can find are two letters from you to Browns ordering the goods and one letter from Browns acknowledging the orders. Is that all there is?"

Faulkner shuffled his feet. It was reply enough.

"Harold," I said reproachfully, "you've got dozens of technical objections to the way these parts have been made. I don't understand any of them myself, any more than I expect the Judge will—and there's nothing in writing."

"Well," he said defensively, "I always telephoned them to complain. They know what's wrong. I've told them twenty times."

"Have you any idea why they've done the work so badly?"

"Frankly Bill, I don't think they had the degree of skill which they needed to do this work. It is rather tricky."

"That sounds all right," I said. Then I pushed my chair back and tried to push my voice down an octave lower to make it more fatherly and admonitory. "Now Harold, how is it that after the trouble started, you've done all your dealings with Browns by telephone, with no record of what you said and no letters?"

A long silence. I could feel Faulkner feeling sheepish. I went on being fatherly:

"Remember in the previous cases, Harold, you saw for yourself how much the Judges like it when you business-men do things in an orderly manner. When goods arrive and they're faulty, you return them with a letter saying why. Each time you return them, you send a letter saying why. Your letters are always to be courteous and must show a quite abnormal reasonableness.

"Then when the case comes to trial, the Judge follows the sequence of events, and he's more than half on your side, because you've followed the rules. Remember the story of Eric, Harold? There's a lot in that for would-be litigants."

"I know all that Bill," Faulkner answered in a recovered voice. "But if business had to work day by day according to the rules laid down by lawyers, we should all be bankrupt. Business people have to trust each other and sometimes there just isn't time to make notes of telephone conversations and to write letters. I know it's all wrong from your point of view, but that's how it is."

He was getting cheeky. I let my voice return to its normal pitch and got in a dig. "Then you mustn't complain when your system breaks down. It's no good coming to me then and demanding an answer. I can't tell you what a Judge will decide in this case because too much depends on how the evidence comes out at the trial. There aren't any documents to rely on apart from the original contract. Now everything turns on what view the Judge forms of you and Brown in the witness-box when you give your evidence."

"Yes, but what about the sample? The goods just don't match up to the sample," he said.

"I know that. But I don't know what Brown will say in the witness-box. He might say for example, that you agreed to accept the goods as they were, because they were near enough. Or he might say that you telephoned him to alter the sample and that the goods are made according to the altered sample. But I don't know what he might say. The point is that if you'd kept notes and confirmed telephone conversations by letter, this difficulty would be less likely to arise. Now it's just your word against his."

There was another long silence. Faulkner was getting the point.

"Tell me," I said. "Are these goods of any use to you as they are?"

"Well," he said hesitantly, "they might be, if we could get some alterations done."

"What would it cost to get them altered, not by Browns but by someone else?"

"I don't know offhand, but I should think about £300," he replied.

"Well look, Browns are claiming just over £1,200. You find out exactly what it'll cost to get these parts put right and let me know and I'll write Browns and offer them the amount of their claim less what you have to pay for the alterations. That'll do the trick, won't it?"

"Well," he said doubtfully, "if they'll accept it."

"Isn't it worth trying?" I asked.

"All right," he said, "try."

Two days later he telephoned to tell me that he could get the job done for £280 and I wrote and offered Browns £900 in settlement. They eventually agreed to accept £950. So Faulkner got his parts, Browns got most of their money and my firm got their costs. But Faulkner wasn't very happy about it. He thought Browns had diddled him. And I don't suppose Browns were any happier. No doubt they thought Faulkner had cheated them. But my firm didn't complain.

Then we lost a case which we should have won. It happens frequently enough, though this knowledge never helps at the time. Henry and I had both been involved in it and we were feeling particularly irritated because this defeat upset our most cherished principle, which is that hard work wins cases.

Nor is this the truism it might sound. We had done a mass of detailed work, had investigated everything that seemed remotely relevant. The documents were neutral and as everything turned on the witnesses, we had taken elaborate proofs from them, leaving nothing to chance. Or so we thought. But sometimes, particularly with some Judges, a small point turns up which nobody has thought about and cases are won or lost on such points, because they suddenly tend to take on a new significance at the trial. Henry and I were experts on small points. We laid every point that ever showed its nose—except in this case. Why nobody thought of it, I don't know, but we all missed it. Henry and I and Counsel as well as the other solicitor and Counsel. But the Judge saw it, took it, and played with it until suddenly it blazed with a terrible light and we lost.

We sauntered back moodily to my room and had some coffee and to cheer myself up, I gave him Wilson's file. I had kept it against such a day as this. "We act for Wilson," I said. "It's a building claim. The builders got a judgment against him, but we got it set aside and now we've got to put in a Defence and Counterclaim. I've already had one extension of time but try and settle it if you can. You know what the costs are like in these cases."

He nodded. "What's the counterclaim for?"

"He had to call in another builder to put the bad work right. We can counterclaim for that, can't we?"

"Oh yes, that's all right," he replied. "Have we got details of what the other builder had to do?"

"Yes, we've got an account from him."

"How are we going to prove that the Plaintiffs did the work badly?" he asked.

"Wilson called in a surveyor. You'll find his report in the file. The report shows all the things that were done wrong."

He nodded again.

"Do settle it if you possibly can," I urged. "I think you'll find that Wilson feels a bit upset at the way he's been treated and I don't blame him, but if he would agree to pay half the claim, the Plaintiffs might take it. And I'm sure it would be cheaper for him to settle for half now, than win after a five-day hearing. Don't you think?"

"Very well," he said. "I'll see how he feels about settling."

"Yes," I replied, "do. You may have to get him in to do a bit of persuading. But for goodness sake, don't take him to lunch, because he's got false teeth and they click all the time he's eating."

Henry sniffed. He also had false teeth, but his didn't click.

He'd hardly been gone five minutes before he was back. He said stiffly, "I'm sorry, but I forgot to mention Mrs. Hill's case."

I could see perfectly well that he hadn't forgotten. He had been preparing for a moment to catch me out and he thought this was it. I collected all the defences I could muster but I did it rather ruefully. When Henry wanted to catch me out, there was usually nothing I could do except watch admiringly or furiously, according to mood.

I looked at him, manœuvring for time. Mrs. Hill? All I could remember was that she was a tall bony woman who looked to be of the landlady class and that she had a straightforward case of desertion and adultery on which she'd recently been granted a decree.

"Well, what about Mrs. Hill?" I said at last. Whatever it was he had up his sleeve, I had no inkling of it.

"Her husband died a few days ago," he said in a neutral voice. This was when Henry was most dangerous, when he used this voice. Somewhere he had a knife on him and he was going to stick it into me at the right moment. I waited as long as I could. Finally I said, when it was clear he wasn't going to say any more: "And you'd just got the decree nisi?"

He nodded but said nothing. He was still waiting for his moment. Something had to give. I gave.

"Then you'd better tell Mrs. Hill there's nothing more we can do for her, hadn't you?" I suggested, wondering what was to come. He knew all this without me saying it. And I added, "After all, she's got what she wants. She's free of her husband."

"Mrs. Hill doesn't think so." Still neutral but now ready to strike. I could almost feel that knife.

"What doesn't she think?"

"Well she didn't want a dead husband, just a divorced one," he replied with the steel entering his voice, "because there is, you will remember, the little matter of maintenance."

"Whatever are you saying, Henry?" I objected, raising my voice, "I didn't kill the man."

"She thinks you did," he said evenly. And there I was, nailed to my own commandment. How often had I said to him in discussing our evidence: "It doesn't matter what happened Henry. What matters is what they think happened. Because what they think happened is what they're going to say happened and that's the evidence coming before the Court—and not what really happened."

But he wasn't just playing words. He'd got me cornered somehow. I still couldn't see how. I laughed shortly. "I killed him? How could I have killed him? I've never even seen him."

He moved closer to my chair. "She's here now," he said almost with a leer, "with a friend, waiting to see you."

"Now?" I said. "But it's five o'clock and she's come without an appointment. I can't see her just because she comes marching into the office like this."

He didn't answer. Why should he? He knew I'd see her. But I wasn't going to see her without knowing a bit more.

"Has she been here long?" I asked.

"She came at half-past two, according to Joan."

So he'd known ever since we came out of Court. He hadn't said a word until now, and we'd spent nearly an hour together. I should have to watch my step. This must be something really big he'd planned.

"You've spoken to her?"

"Yes, I thought she'd come to see me," he replied.

"But she hadn't," I said in a flat voice. "She'd come to see me." He nodded.

"With a friend," I went on, feeling my way. Ah, the friend. That was it. I could feel the satisfaction exuding from him at the mention of the word.

187

"Who's the friend?" I asked casually. He hesitated and again I knew that here was the clue. But he had to tell me. The rules demanded that. If I could get out of it by doing the correct thing, he wasn't allowed to mislead me.

He played fair: "She's a medium, I believe."

I stared at him. "A medium?" I was astonished. We get some pretty odd fish but I'd never known a client bring an adviser of this kind before.

"Why?" I asked. "Why a medium?"

He opened out. The game was up anyway. He made a triumphant explanation: "Well the other evening after the funeral, Mrs. Hill went to a seance at the medium's house, and she appears to have been told by a spirit that divorce is the murder of a relationship and that the spirit of the divorced person always dies with the death of the marriage. And sometimes when the divorced person is a very spiritual person his body dies also. And that's why Mr. Hill died. He'd been murdered by the divorce. That is what the spirit told Mrs. Hill and as you'd advised her to divorce him, she thinks you're the murderer."

"But that's stuff and nonsense. The chap had been living in adultery with another woman for years and years," I said angrily.

Henry had relaxed. The joke was over for him.

But I still had to get out of it.

"This," I said firmly, "is Mr. Gissing's line of country."

I reached for the internal telephone and asked George if he could spare a moment. When he came in, I said: "George, I think we have always agreed that everything pertaining to the passing over of people is your field and not mine?"

He was puzzled. "Well, yes, I suppose so," he said. "Henry," I went on, "has two people waiting to see you on a matter which falls within that field."

I opened the door and pushed them out. Then I lay back in my chair sweating. It had been a near thing.

Later George told me that the two ladies had been charming and that he'd taken instructions to make their Wills. He never said anything else about it and I never asked him. But Henry kept out of my way for weeks.

Several new cases turned up including two more divorces. The Petitioner in each case was a woman, and the grounds in each case were adultery. They both alleged excessive sexual demands by their husbands and both had to be restrained from proceeding against their husbands for cruelty, because investigation showed that there wasn't any case for cruelty. This seems to be a perennial complaint by women Petitioners against their husbands. Either the men of this country are extraordinarily virile, which I very much doubt, or the women are extraordinarily disinterested, which sounds more likely. I should think this must also be a very English complaint.

I had a very curious interview one day with an attractive young girl who came to see me about a divorce.

"What are the grounds?" I asked.

She hesitated for a moment. "My husband won't wash," she said.

"Won't wash? Why not?" I asked.

"I don't really know," she said. "I've asked him but he doesn't answer."

I looked at her. She seemed perfectly normal.

"When was the last time he washed?" I asked.

She thought: "About six weeks ago," she replied.

"Six weeks!"

She nodded.

"But doesn't he work?" I asked.

"Oh yes," she replied smiling, "he shaves and washes his face when he goes to work."

"Then what parts of him doesn't he wash?"

"Mostly his feet. He sits on the bed and peels the scales off them," she said evenly.

I gazed at her, horrified. It didn't look as if she minded much.

"How long has this been going on for?" I demanded.

"Ever since we've been married."

"But that's four years," I couldn't stop myself saying.

She nodded.

If you'd passed her in the street you would never have believed that for four years she'd watched her husband peeling scales of dirt from his feet. She looked too clean and wholesome to be mixed up in anything like that and yet I could have sworn she didn't mind much.

"Don't you mind that he's dirty?"

She shrugged: "I didn't until recently."

"What happened recently?" I asked, though I knew the answer before she coloured.

"Dirty habits are not a ground for divorce," I told her, "unless you can show they amount to cruelty and in your case they don't. You look too healthy. They might perhaps be a good reason for leaving him, but that's up to you."

And she went away to think about it. I never saw her again. But I often thought of those feet and the scales being pulled off one by one, while she lay there in the bed idly watching.

George had seen Chirpy Bird about the Agency agreement and he related to me the instructions which Bird had given him.

"Draw an agreement," Bird had said, "but do it so that we can get out of it if we want to."

"Well, in what circumstances are you likely to want to get out of it?" George had wanted to know.

Bird had said patiently: "You see we don't want to be sued if for any reason anything should go wrong on our side." I could imagine George's face as he said this. George had replied equally patiently.

"You know of course that the whole point of a contract is to bind both sides to carry out the matter agreed upon."

"Oh yes," Bird had nodded approvingly. "We want to bind them all right."

"But you don't want to be bound yourselves," George had finished the sentence for him.

"That's right," Bird had said.

From what George told me the interview hadn't lasted very long after that.

I saw a woman who wanted to bring a nullity suit against her husband. There must be a very considerable number of marriages which have never been consummated and I was always surprised how normal the people involved seemed to the outsider. I was surprised too, how long people tended to wait before they did anything about it. This particular woman was in her late twenties, smart, attractive and apparently, desirable enough. She'd been married over seven years to an advertising man, and we talked about him for a while. If she hadn't told me at the outset why she had come, I would have thought her to be a perfectly normally married young woman. She appeared to be relaxed, there was no tension about her, but she talked impersonally as if it was all about somebody else. Until we got down to the issue. Then her composure wavered and she began to search for words and flutter her hands.

The point seemed to be her husband's ambition. He was going to get on and nothing was to be allowed to stand in the way. She said he'd told her this before they were married, but what he hadn't told her was that he believed that sexual relations were weakening. He had to be first rate, he said and she thought he wasn't altogether sure he was. If he used his energy on sexual intercourse with her, he would have less to drive him forward, and he couldn't afford to risk being left behind. So the marriage had never been consummated and now he was earning £5,000 a year and expenses.

"Why have you waited so long?" I asked quietly.

"Well I saw his point," she said reasonably. "And I wanted him to be happy and I thought that once he'd proved himself, it would be all right."

"And has he proved himself?" I asked gently.

"I should have thought so," she returned wearily, "but I haven't been able to get near him now for a long time. Either he's working or we're away with friends for the week-end or we're out at some function, or we have people with us. I never see him alone." She smiled sadly. "Except in bed and that's no good as I've told you."

"Why have you now decided to start proceedings?" I asked politely.

"Because I'm twenty-nine," she said defensively.

I had expected more, but that wasn't my business until we got to the question of discretion and that wasn't yet. "You know," I said blandly, "that a nullity suit might be a bit damaging to your husband if it got about in his circle. It isn't the happiest thing that can be said about a man, that he couldn't consummate his marriage, particularly in a competitive society like the advertising world where a man probably has more enemies than he can watch all the time."

Her lips tightened. She knew about this. "Yes," she said stiffly. "I know that."

This was a bit odd. She didn't look as if she wanted to pay him out. She didn't look that kind of person, unless . . . I stopped at that. She ought to be pressed a little further. There was no sense in causing damage if it could be avoided.

"Have you told your husband what you intend?" I asked casually.

"Of course I've told him," she said quickly, almost passionately. Whatever the block had been, it had gone.

"Do you think I want to bring a nullity suit? All I want is to put an end to this situation. I don't care how it's done."

"What did he say when you told him?"

She smiled a queer, hard smile: "He just shrugged," she said.

"Didn't he say anything?"

"He was just very superior. He's been like that for some time now," she answered. "He knows he can get someone to play hostess to his friends, or rather his business acquaintances—he hasn't got any friends. And I suppose he thinks he can explain it all away quite easily." She sat back in her chair staring in front of her. She wasn't happy about it, even now.

What a nice woman, I thought. But she couldn't do any more than she'd done.

"All right," I said. "Nullity it is. Now let's get it down."

I drew the Petition myself. It was very simple and after it had been served on the husband, I persuaded Henry to issue a Summons in the Divorce Division to appoint a medical inspector. Henry agreed with a bad grace, but he didn't stay long in my room to argue. He was afraid I might make a joke about it, and that he wanted to avoid at all costs.

The Order making the appointment was rather striking:

IT IS ORDERED that William Bloggs-Bloggs M.B.B.S. be appointed as Inspector to examine the parts and organs of generation of the above-named Respondent in this cause, to report in writing whether he is capable of performing the act of generation, and if incapable of so doing whether such his impotency can or cannot be relieved or removed by art or skill. AND also to examine the parts and organs of generation of the above named Petitioner in this cause and to report in writing whether she is or is not a virgin, and hath or hath not any impediment on her part to prevent the consummation of marriage and whether such impediment (if any) can or cannot be removed by art or skill.

And a week later the Petitioner and I went to Somerset House and Dr. Bloggs-Bloggs examined her in a private room and reported to the Court that he had found that "she is apparently capable of performing the act of generation". It seemed to me a very appealing phrase.

Some time later, after she'd been granted a decree of Nullity, I received an invitation to attend her wedding. I wrote a polite note declining. I receive half a dozen or so invitations a year from clients who are re-marrying. I often wonder why they think it necessary to invite me. Perhaps it is an act of propitiation. Hopman thinks it's to get back some of the costs they've paid as wedding presents, but I don't believe that. A good many other solicitors I know also get them. One man who always goes to these weddings has an arrangement with a pawnbroker to buy cheap all the sets of fish-knives that come into his shop. I thought fish-knives had gone out of fashion as wedding presents, but this chap is a great success with his.

George also passed over a few new cases to me. Two breaches of contract, a few boring debts to collect and a libel action. The libel action was a beauty, the very stuff of which philosophies are created, expounded and then silenced.

Louise and Emma were two middle-aged women who lived in small country towns a hundred miles from each other. They met twice a year in London, where they spent a happy day together at a matinée, at a restaurant, in their Ladies' Club, in shopping and in gossip. They had been friends since their schooldays and they were always interested in the lives of the girls who had been at school with them. And long chatty letters passed between them every week.

One day, Louise received a letter from Emma which began in this arresting way:

"My dear, what do you think? You must remember little Sybil Spittle that was. She's just come to live here—in a very grand house. And who do you think her new husband is? You'll never guess. It's that man Edward used all those nasty words about—you know, George Dent. When she told me her new name, I couldn't wait until I'd got the whole story out of her. She's only just married him. He's only after her money of course, if she's got any left after what it cost her to get rid of Jack. And she doesn't know anything about her husband. I pumped her until I was hoarse. <u>Poor</u> Sybil. And she seems to be <u>so</u> happy too. Of course I didn't tell her <u>anything</u>."

Louise was delighted when she read this. She couldn't wait to show the letter to her husband.

Edward grunted when she said:

"You must read Emma's letter darling. It's about my old school friend Sybil Spittle that was."

And with a great effort, she said no more. She was longing for him to read the hated name and burst into a roar. But Edward said:

"I can't read Emma's letters. She only writes one paragraph and it's always ten thousand words long."

"Darling," Louise simpered using her best coaxing voice. "I'm sure you'll find it very interesting."

Edward couldn't bear Louise when she used this voice. It reminded him of the day when as a child he had yielded to a small girl's coaxing to tear a piece of cardboard with his teeth. So he took the letter, because his teeth were on edge again, as once they had been forty years earlier. And as before, the coaxing proved his undoing.

"Why does she have to underline all these words?" was all he said in a bad-tempered voice. And then he said loudly in a very different, angry tone:

"She couldn't have married that crooked swine. Why he ruined Harry's business, pinched his patents and then made a fortune out of them for himself."

He looked at Louise with a purple face: "This stinking bastard ought to be in prison, safely locked away from decent people. I'm sorry for your friend Louise, but she ought to know what kind of a man she's married." There was a good deal more of this and Louise drank in every word. She could hardly wait until Edward was out of the house next morning and then she wrote to Emma and repeated everything which Edward had told her. And unfortunately it happened to be untrue.

Harry's business had certainly been ruined, but Harry himself had done the ruining and being a weak little man had laid the blame at George Dent's door and everybody including Edward had believed him.

But one more link in the chain had yet to be forged before a

194

Writ for libel would lie on my desk. And the chain became complete the day Emma called to have tea with Sybil and left her handbag behind her. Now Emma was not a forgetful person and perhaps had mislaid her handbag two or three times in her whole life and it was remarkable that one of those times should have been at Sybil's house. But it was.

Sybil gave the bag to her daily help who having cooked the dinner was about to go home and had promised to drop the bag in to Emma on her way. As she was standing about in the kitchen getting herself ready to go, she remembered that she had to buy some groceries in the morning and decided to make a note to remind herself. She looked unsuccessfully for a pencil and her eye caught Emma's bag. There could be no harm in borrowing a pencil for a moment. As she opened the bag to look, she drew out the contents, and the words "and Sybil's husband George . . ." caught her eye. The rest is simply told. She went into the sitting-room and said to Sybil: "Ma'am, I think you ought to see this."

And that is why my partner had asked me to deal with a libel action. George Dent was suing Louise for publishing a libel of him to Emma. He was not suing Edward though Edward had in the first place been responsible for the story getting about. But English Law so highly esteems the confidence which spouse may repose in spouse that it holds that a man and his wife may say what they will to each other about other people and be free of responsibility. So Edward's slander went unheeded. And Dent was not suing Emma because he didn't know about Emma's first letter to Louise which had pricked Edward to disaster.

It took me some time to discover all this and when I learned that George Dent hadn't cheated Harry, it was clear that there was no answer to the libel. It took me more time to convince Edward of this. He thought it was very hard that Louise should be liable for something he had honestly believed to be true. But it would have been harder on Dent, if she hadn't been liable and they had to face up to the fact that there was no defence.

I saw George Dent's solicitor several times and eventually Dent agreed to drop the action if Louise would pay £100 to a charity and his costs, and make a statement in Court apologising. There wasn't very much we could do but agree. The damages would have been much higher if Dent had gone to trial, and the costs would certainly have been greater. And Edward and Louise finally agreed. So a gossipy letter cost Edward about £200 and a very red face. It was also the end of a beautiful friendship.

I have heard that gossip as a pastime is dying out because everyone is so busy watching television that there's no time to talk about anybody. I hope this isn't true. Nothing is quite so exciting or so profitable as a well-directed piece of scandal.

But apart from the new work, all the old work went on. The Ward of Court Order in Diggins' case was rescinded and the Diggins family went back to Australia.

I had a short letter from Mrs. Green: "My husband has asked me to let you know that we have been reconciled. He does not wish you to take any further steps."

And that was all. Green had surrendered to his wife's threat of suicide. Now there would again be woe and misery in the land, more human sacrifice, more cannibalism, but no voice would be raised on Green's behalf by the men and women of good will; there would be no intercession from the small back rooms up and down the streets behind the Strand. Mrs. Green could devour him without interruption.

I saw Nixon again and we went over the same old ground without ever coming to a conclusion. Eventually he'd make a decision, but it would have to be in his own time. I was in no hurry myself.

There had been no reply to the letter I had drafted for White to send his wife. I drafted another. To this she had replied and they had met in the lounge of the Dorchester Hotel and had a talk, a very friendly talk, he said. He told me that he thought it would be good for them to live separately for a bit longer and to meet once a week to see how they got on. What did I think of that? I said that if that's what they wanted, I thought it was a good idea. Yes, but what did I really think? But what I thought was what Willie Vincent had told me and although for a reason I did not know, I carefully kept his words out of my mind, I was watchful nevertheless.

I listened twice to what Mrs. Gray had to tell me about her family and I received Sheila Smith's latest progress reports of no progress.

I had a stormy interview with Campbell who had been

knocked down by a car and rather badly hurt. The car-driver's insurance company had offered £750 to settle the claim.

"Look," I said, "it's not my money. I don't care personally whether you take £750 or not. But your case is worth more than £750. I can't guarantee that you'll win outright if you go to trial, but you ought to get more than that, even if the Judge finds you were partly to blame for the accident."

"What do you think I'd get?" he asked greedily.

"If the Judge finds you weren't negligent, between £2,000 and £2,500. If he does find you partly to blame, I can't see that it could be more than 50% at the worst, and it might be a good deal better than that. So you'll get whatever the Judge awards less 50% at the worst, and if he finds you weren't to blame at all, you'll get the lot. I don't see how you can possibly get less than £750 at the trial and you ought to get a good deal more. So the Insurance Company aren't giving much away by offering you £750, are they? They ought to pay more, if they want to settle."

"Isn't there any chance of me losing altogether?" he asked.

"Well, litigation is always a risk, but I should have thought there was very little chance in this case of getting less than £750."

He leaned back in his chair. He was stroking the bird in his hand and looking at the two in the bush.

"If I decide to go on," he said finally, "how long will it take before the case is heard in Court?"

"Between nine months to a year."

He shook his head. "I can't wait that long. I want it now."

"Supposing I can get the offer increased?" I asked. "You wouldn't refuse it, would you?"

He looked at me as if I were mad.

"I think I can probably get it increased," I said, "if you give me time. If I rush at the Insurance Company, they won't pay any more, because they'll know you want to settle. But if I refuse their offer, they may very well make another one. It takes time though, and you run a certain risk. And the risk is that if we refuse their offer and they don't make another one, you can't then accept the £750 because that offer's gone. I don't think myself that there's any risk worth talking about, because I should imagine in this case that they'll be prepared to offer £750 at any time. But you ought to know the position."

"That settles it," he said firmly. "I'll take the £750."

I made a last effort. "Look here, I'm pretty certain if you give me a bit more time, say a fortnight, I can get you more than £750. Will you do it?"

But I could see he wouldn't. I didn't really blame him. He didn't know the ways of Insurance Companies and £750 now, might conceivably be more valuable to him than twice as much in a year's time. But still I couldn't bear to see him take less than half the value of his claim, so I said: "Would you agree to me ringing them now to see if I can get a bit more?"

He said rather doubtfully, "All right."

Fortunately Williams was in. I came straight to the point. It was bad tactics, but I couldn't see what else to do.

"Williams we'll take £1,000 and costs, but not a penny less."

"All right old man, I'll see what I can do."

"You'll have to do it fast, Williams. I've got instructions to settle for £1,000 and costs today or I must issue a Writ. My client won't wait any longer."

I could tell from Williams' voice that he'd pay. He'd probably got instructions sitting in his file to go up to £1,000. But the form required him to say:

"I'll get instructions and ring you back."

"Before 3.30 please Williams, if I'm to get the Writ issued today."

"All right old man."

Campbell's eyes were popping out. I'd lost him his £750. I said to him shortly: "If you'll please ring me after four today, I'll let you know. Don't worry. It'll be all right. I know this company fairly well. If they won't pay £1,000 I'll settle for £750."

"But you said if I refused that offer, it was gone." He was so panicky, he could hardly speak coherently.

"I know. But that's the theory of it. In practice, in a case like this, they will renew it. Don't worry, you'll get your £750. But they ought to pay £1,000."

And they did. Williams knew a good thing when he saw it. And to settle a £2,000 claim for £1,000 was a good thing for him and his company. But it irritated me very much. Sometimes I got sick of my clients and their ways.

I had briefed Somes to defend Smithers at Sessions. I had also seen Smithers' girl friend and got a statement of her evidence. She was a pretty rather unsophisticated fair girl, obviously honest. She was very upset by the charge of gross indecency, but she believed every word Smithers said and she looked as if she might make a good witness. She confirmed that Smithers had spent the evening with her and left her just before eleven o'clock. She clearly wasn't sleeping with him which was rather a pity. We should have had a very striking defence if we could have shown that they'd made love together on the evening when Smithers had been charged. I should have enjoyed watching the Prosecution trying to prove that Smithers had been engaged in mutual masturbation with a man half an hour afterwards. I had never before heard of such a defence being used and I have no idea what effect it might have had if it had been. I dare say the newspapers would have enjoyed it. But anyway we couldn't use it.

We had a conference with Somes who was more optimistic than I'd been. He was pretty certain that even if Smithers were convicted, there would only be a fine. I hoped he was right. But he did a good deal of this kind of work and he should have known.

At ten o'clock on the morning of the trial, I met Somes at the Court. He said that he'd been talking to Dunton, Robinson's Counsel, and there wasn't so much conflict between the stories after all.

"We say," he said, "that Smithers lost the back buttons off his trousers and that he went into the lavatory to tie his braces round them. Then Robinson offered him some string. Smithers tried to tie the string round his trousers by himself and keep them up at the same time and couldn't, and his trousers fell down. Robinson offered to lend him a hand." He sniggered briefly, recovered and went on stiffly: "Smithers stood there holding his trousers up with both hands and Robinson came close to him to tie the string round. So far our stories tally, don't they?"

I nodded.

"Also," he went on, "that is what Smithers told the police. They've got all that down in the statement he made. But that's all he told them." He paused to let this sink in.

Somes was a tall, very thin man and he'd been bending down towards me as he spoke. Now he straightened his back. He had a thick mass of wiry grey hair which never seemed to be combed properly. When he straightened up, he looked like an inverted mop.

"The only difference between our stories," he said nonchalantly, waving his hand, "is that Smithers says Robinson touched him and Robinson says he didn't, but now he also says that if he did touch him it was accidental."

"But Smithers won't say it was accidental," I objected.

"He'll say it was deliberate."

Somes had the kind of voice which you don't normally associate with a mop. It was heavy and expensive, a marron glacé voice. Now it got fuzzy at the edges. Somes didn't like to be misunderstood.

"There was perhaps a minute between the time Robinson came over to Smithers and the time the police made the arrest," he explained in this suffering fools as gladly as he could voice. "It looked suspicious to the police to see two men standing so close together, but we can explain that. I know Smithers thinks that Robinson was trying to interfere with him and if that's what he thinks, that's what he'll have to say, if he's asked. But all I'm trying to show you is that the two stories aren't so far apart as we first thought."

"I see it now," I said. "You're not going to ask Smithers. You're going to keep the indecent assault out if you can."

When he replied, his voice was fruity again. I had understood. He was quite right of course. Our job was to get Smithers off. We had to present our case in the best way possible and it was important to avoid any conflict in the evidence of the two Accused if we could. It wasn't our job to present the police with a prosecution against Robinson. If I'd been the advocate myself, I would have missed this and gone blundering on; an argument, I supposed, for keeping the professions separate. But a better argument would be that I should keep out of the Criminal Courts.

"Fortunately," Somes said, "there aren't any other gross indecencies in the List today and we should be on by eleven. There's only sentence to be pronounced in two receiving cases and an application."

After the Jury had been sworn in, our case was called. I looked carefully at the jury. They were all men, because ours was a dirty case. It was hard to tell at that stage what they were like as individual people, just as it is when you first look at a platoon of soldiers. It takes a bit of time to break them down into units.

The foreman was a bouncy-looking little man with fair hair who didn't look very sympathetic, but there were several friendly-looking men sitting solemnly in the jury box. And as the evidence was taken, I watched the play of expression on their faces. We only wanted one of them on our side and if he were strong enough, he would win for us.

Chindle was prosecuting again. He opened his case to the jury and told them what his witnesses would prove in their evidence. He referred several times to the "disgusting offence with which these men are charged".

And he appeared to mean what he said. He'd forgotten the antics he'd got up to at school when it was all rather a lark, Now it was Section 11 of the Criminal Law Amendment Act, 1885.

He called his two policemen. They gave the same evidence as they had given at the Magistrates' Court. Under cross-examination they were both quite certain what they had seen. They had seen mutual masturbation. There was no possibility of mistake, though they agreed that the light had not been good. They gave different versions of the time they had actually observed the Accused committing the offence. The tall thick constable who had gone into the lavatory first, said that he had observed what was happening for 30 seconds before he made the arrest. The short thick constable who had followed him in, said that he had watched for well over a minute.

The second constable was rather damaged by Somes' cross-examination.

"You followed your colleague into the lavatory?" Somes asked.

"Yessir."

"You say you were watching in the lavatory for well over a minute?"

"Yessir."

"But your colleague says he only watched for half a minute before he made the arrest."

The Constable was silent and then he said: "I may be wrong sir. It may only have been half a minute."

"You didn't look at your watch to check the length of your observation?"

"No sir."

"You kept observation in the doorway of the lavatory?"

"Yessir."

"How wide is the doorway?"

"About three feet, I'd say sir."

"Wide enough for two of you to stand in, side by side?"

The answer was slower this time. The Constable could feel a trap closing in, but couldn't yet see what it was. He moved his head from side to side slowly.

Then he said: "No sir."

"You mean you would have to stand behind your colleague?"

"Yessir."

"And did you stand behind him?"

"Yessir."

"But he's taller than you are. He blocked your view completely, didn't he?"

"No sir." The poor chap began to wag his head again.

Somes pressed the advantage home. "How much taller is your colleague than you?"

Everybody looked at the first constable who went scarlet.

"About a foot sir."

"If you stand behind him, how far up his body do you reach?"

The Constable decided it would be safer to stonewall.

"I don't know sir."

Somes asked the first Constable to stand in front of the witness. The effect was startling. The eyes of the witness were on a level with the first man's shoulder-blades. I looked quickly at the jury. They'd all seen the point. The foreman had yellow hairs sticking out of his nose and he was twirling them.

Somes now had enough to hammer the wilting Constable and he hammered him. By the time he'd finished, there was nothing left of his evidence. For half a minute he'd stood in the doorway behind a taller man's back. Smithers whose back he had been facing was also bigger than he was. And yet he still said he'd seen the Accused masturbate each other. And I had no doubt in my own mind that the policeman was honest and thought he was telling the truth, his truth. But it was clear that the jury had their doubts.

When Dunton rose to cross-examine, there was nothing else to say, so having got up, he sat down again and said, "No questions."

Somes had done it. He had virtually destroyed the corroboration of the first Constable's evidence and juries understandably don't like convicting for gross indecency without corroboration. Now if only the Accused gave their evidence well, it looked as if we should win.

One of the reasons why I disliked criminal work was because of my too personal interest in it. I was mostly detached enough while I was preparing the defence for trial but once the trial had started, I ceased to be an onlooker. The drama was not merely happening to somebody else. It was also happening to me.

So I watched Smithers go into the box anxiously. But he was all right and his girl friend made a good impression. I could wish always to have a pretty girl as a witness in my cases, particularly when there's a jury or the Judge is very old.

Oddly enough, Robinson made a better impression than Smithers. Nothing had been said by Smithers about Robinson's interference. Somes didn't ask him and it hadn't occurred to Chindle to ask. There was no reason why it should. By good fortune, Smithers' incoherence on the night of the offence had resulted in him leaving out of his statement to the police what he had thought was the most important part. Chindle had got as far as asking Smithers:

"You say that you and the other Accused were not interfering with each other?"

"We were not," Smithers had said and it was true. Robinson confirmed Smithers' story and said that he'd lent him some string and offered to tie up his trousers when Smithers obviously couldn't manage by himself and at that point the constables had come in to the lavatory. The story rang truly which was in itself an advantage when so often the truth doesn't sound very true.

After the closing speeches and the summing up, the Jury retired. I always found this wait pretty nearly unbearable. All the time I felt like a little boy wanting to go to the lavatory and not liking to say so. Which in the circumstances of the present case was perhaps not altogether incongruous.

We walked up and down the passage outside the Court. Smithers and Robinson had been taken down to the cells to wait.

Somes said:

"If they come back within half an hour, it's usually an acquittal. After half an hour, it's usually a conviction. After an hour it can be one or the other but more probably an acquittal."

Dunton said: "I like it better if they return within half an hour. Then it's almost always an acquittal. But after an hour, it's more often than not a conviction."

And they began to give each other examples. I walked up and down by myself. I worked out the binomial theorem to the seventh power, then I said the seventeen times table to myself. I recited bits of the XXXth Canto because it seemed appropriate and by the time the jury had been gone forty minutes, I had got round to Henry V's speech on St. Crispin's Day and was whispering:

> He which hath no stomach to this fight.
> Let him depart

when the word went round that the jury was back.

We all filed into the Court and I looked at the faces in the Jury box, old, young, fine, coarse, fair, dark, hairy and smooth. How was Smithers going to manage if he were convicted?

The Clerk said: "Members of the Jury, are you agreed upon your verdict?"

"We are," said the foreman.

And then I heard the words "Not Guilty", and felt sweaty again.

After everybody had shaken hands with everybody else, Robinson came over to me. "I was very impressed," he said in what I was sure was his most sincere voice, "with the way you handled this case."

I looked at him with distaste. I had heard this kind of thing before. It was softening-up talk. People said it when they wanted something. I waited to hear what it was he wanted.

He didn't appear to be put out by his reception. "I wanted to ask if you'd act for me," he said simply.

"But you've got a solicitor," I replied bluntly.

He shook his head.

"What is it exactly you want me to do?" I asked uneasily.

"Oh, it's nothing much. I shall soon be taking a new flat, that's all. I shall want a solicitor."

I was so relieved that I gave him George's name without another thought. "My partner," I said, "deals with that kind of thing."

Some little time later, George came into my room and held out a letter. It was from a firm of Estate Agents:

"We have been given your name by your client Mr. George Robinson who wishes to take the tenancy of a flat from a client of ours at a rental of £300 per annum. We should be glad if you would be good enough to say whether from your knowledge of your client he is likely to prove a responsible and respectable tenant able to meet the liabilities arising from his occupation of the flat and willing to honour the usual tenant's covenants."

I began to laugh.

"Who is he?" George demanded.

"It's the fellow who was charged with Smithers," I said and told him about my conversation with Robinson.

"How can I give him a reference?" George asked plaintively. "I've never seen the man and all I know of him is that he hangs around public lavatories committing indecent acts."

"Now George," I said warningly, "he was acquitted."

And then I laughed again. "After all," I said, "really who better than us to confirm his respectability? We saw him acquitted. We can positively guarantee him."

"But I thought Smithers said that Robinson had interfered with him," George replied tartly.

"Yes, I know George," I said. "I was only teasing. You can't give a reference, because you don't know him and I won't give a reference because I do."

And we never heard of Robinson again.

Vᴵɴɢᴛᴏᴛ ɢᴏᴛ sɪᴄᴋ of staying at the hostel and for the last week of his course, he came to stay with us. On the night of his departure I went to the station with him. He was going back to Paris without his French accent. Whoever Professor Pumper was, he had done wonders. Vingtot was now left with an accent which was vaguely foreign, but no longer distinctively French. His 'o's' were startlingly English and disturbed the rhythm of his voice. I complained to him.

"It used to be a pleasure listening to you speak English. Now you sound like a bloody Eurasian."

"What does a Eurasian sound like?" he asked, looking pleased. No doubt I was paying him a high compliment.

"Just like you," I said rudely. "When you speak English now, people will think you're the product of a passionate night in Algiers."

He stopped looking pleased. "But Professor Pumper assured me . . ." he said and then he shrugged and gave up. You could never tell with the English when they were joking and when they were not.

Just before he got into the train, he put on his grave look. He was going to talk about Mary. He only got as far as "My dear friend," when I thanked him warmly for breaking three lamps during his week at the house. "You have no idea," I said, "how grateful I am to you. I break as many lamps as I can, but the rate of replacement is too high for me to manage by myself. I shall always regard what you did as the truest proof of friendship you could have given me." And I shook his hand effusively until the train moved out.

Mary's mother lived in Edinburgh and she was taking the children there for Easter. When I got home after seeing Vingtot off she was packing, ready to leave early next morning. She came into my room on some innocent errand. On her way out she said: "I'm glad M. Vingtot has gone. He's very exhausting, you know."

I should have known that she'd had a tiring evening packing and that Vingtot had caused extra work in the house, that he liked talking to practise his idiom and she didn't. Instead, I said sharply:

"How is it that you don't like anybody? I think Vingtot is a wonderful person."

"There aren't any wonderful people," she said wearily. "There are just people, mouths to feed, voices to answer, demands to fulfil. That's all."

Anger bubbled up inside me. I was about to shout at her when suddenly I felt as if I had been shouted down, though Mary had spoken no word. But I had been shouted down just the same, by a great booming bullying voice. The noise banged against the sides of my head as if it were trying to get out and great fires were burning in my brain. Every part of my body seemed to hurt. A line flitted through my mind, unremembered since childhood: "He must be wicked to deserve such pain."

I sank down into a chair, concentrating my remaining strength on keeping my lips shut. If I opened them, I knew I should groan and that I couldn't have. Anyway I had no reason to open my mouth. What was there to say? Suddenly it was upon me again. The thing was finished. I knew it now.

"Are you all right Bill?" she asked. There was concern in her voice.

I nodded. My head was whirling with strange mad things to say, things I had never said to her before. I could feel the seals falling off the passages I had blocked up in my head, could feel it throbbing with Mary's face and Mary's voice. Words I didn't want to remember, loving words and beastly words, ran up and down me like mice in a grandfather clock.

The minutes passed in a wretched silence. Mary sat in her chair as if she were alone, as indeed she was. As I was. And my head spun with half completed thoughts, with the dog-ends of phrases. To force myself back into some kind of control, I got up and drew the curtains. Nothing moved outside; no living thing stirred. The sky was black and clouded over and no stars twinkled. There was no light anywhere. The world might have been dead.

Words came into my head. I uttered them. I did not know what they were until I heard them. "Are you happy living like this?"

207

She looked up, her face stony. "Happy?" she repeated. "No, I'm not happy. I'm not anything." I was not touched, not hurt for her, not even any more hurt for myself, but I went and put my arms around her. She suffered me, making no response. Then she began to sob, great choking sobs. She cried for what seemed a long time until I began to feel the tears pricking my own eyes. Then she groped for a handkerchief and blew her nose loudly.

There is something about a tearful woman blowing her nose on a too small handkerchief. I gave her mine. She took it and wiped her face and then gave it back to me. But the gesture was social, not tender. She pushed her chair back resolutely and stood up.

"It's no good Bill," she said jerkily, as if her clockwork were running down, "it's no good. We're finished."

And she collapsed into the chair and began to rock up and down as if she were ill. I gave her my handkerchief again and she sobbed into it until I could feel every part of the house throbbing to her misery.

I got her a drink and made her sip it slowly. Then I said gently: "Mary don't cry any more. Please, not any more." And I kissed her.

She sat in the chair looking in front of her hopelessly, her hair disordered, her face broken. Then she turned to me and her nose was red and shining, but her muted voice went straight to my heart:

"Bill," she said, whimpering like a frightened animal, "I don't know what to do any more. I feel everything collapsing over my head and I don't know what to do." I put my arms around her. I didn't have any other answer. I didn't know what to do either.

After a long time, she said quietly: "Bill, do you think it would be better if we separated?"

I said what I thought she expected: "Of course not. What would I do without you?"

"What indeed?" she replied. The old bitter Mary was back. I had failed her again. But I tried, not because I wanted to make it right; I didn't know what I wanted, but I tried because what else was there to do?

"It's been a difficult year for you," I said in as tender a voice as I could find, "and you need a holiday. When you come back and the children are at school, perhaps Henriette could come and stay for a few days and we could go away by ourselves. What do you think?"

At once she became excited and gripped my hand:

"Oh yes," she said gladly, "let's please do that. I'd like it so much." And then her voice took on a pleading, fervent note: "Darling, let's make it like it used to be. I'm sure we can do it, if we try hard enough. Darling, please do let's try and make it happy for us both." And she was weeping noisily again.

But I'd had enough of weeping. I didn't want any bogus surface reconstructions, any more pretences. I wanted it to be honest, even if it were also hopeless. As I watched her crying I felt only distaste. What had all this to do with me? Was I a lobster to throw out a new claw on demand?

She was gripping my hand. Hers was all wet from the tears she had shed and mine felt clammy and uncomfortable. But I let it remain. She raised her face and her tearful eyes were shining with happiness. I was appalled. And as I looked at her face, wondering what to do, I remembered the conversation which I had tried to vomit away, which had been too much for me to keep down. That still had to be faced before the new dawn.

"What about your consolation Mary?" I asked brutally. "What are you going to do about him?"

She stared at me, her mouth open. The words she didn't understand. The tone was altogether too unmistakable. Something else she'd done wrong.

I went on. "You told me a little while ago that you'd been meaning to talk to me about it for a long time but hadn't been able to find a suitable opportunity. Well, here's your opportunity."

Her hand went to her mouth. Her eyes widened, the tears still glistening in them. But it was terror this time.

I can still see her face as it was then. I use it as a reminder when I find myself judging other people. Then I bring it back before my inner eye. If anyone had told me that I would ever behave so as to cause another human being to wear such a mask of misery and fear, I wouldn't have believed I could do it. But I did. If I am tolerant of other people's sins, it is only because I have to live with my own.

Her fright fed my anger.

"You want to make it all lovey-dovey, don't you?" I snarled, "but what about your boy friend? What's he going to say about it, eh?"

She stood up and made a movement towards me, with her hand fluttering, "Bill," she said appealingly, "I . . ."

"Well, what?" I sneered.

She turned on her heel wearily and moved to the door.

I could have left it at that. I had broken her. But it wasn't enough. I rushed in front of her before she could open the door. "I want to know who it is," I roared. "I'm going to know who it is."

She was restored. "Why?" she asked coolly. "What good will it do you?"

"I don't care whether it does me any good or not. I want to know."

She shook her head. "I'm not telling you," she said firmly.

And then I began to behave like one of my own cases and watched myself doing it, helpless, quite utterly helpless to intervene in my own behalf. I shouted at her. "All right if that's how it is, I'll put an end to it. I'll have you watched and as soon as I've got the evidence I'll divorce you."

The word was out. The word I so often used but never about myself, not even in thought, hung in the air between us. I felt terrified, somehow hunted.

If she had then said to me: "You don't really want a divorce, do you?", I would have collapsed with relief at her feet. But she didn't. She took me to mean what I'd said. She tightened her lips: "All right," she said in a hard voice, "if that's what you want."

But I didn't want it. And when I finally got my mouth to open, I meant to say that I didn't want it. Instead I heard myself saying what for a moment I couldn't understand, what seemed to be irrelevant: "Anyway, Vingtot thinks the children would be better off without me. Do you think that too?"

Too late I saw it. Too late the awful relevance became clear. I was repeating the pattern. I was giving her a club and baring my head and I was saying "Hit me." And she did.

"Yes," she said, "I think it too."

I first read Dostoevsky when I was thirteen and I remember at the time that I couldn't believe that people like his characters really existed. It took me a long time to change my mind. But even in my worst moments, I never believed that I would myself become such a character. But even this had happened.

I heard my voice saying: "I won't be here when you get back from Edinburgh." And then my door closed quietly. It was the most final sound I ever heard in my life.

I sat up for the rest of the night playing the gramophone and drinking coffee. And in the morning I left the house before they were up. I was in the office two hours before anybody else arrived. They were all rather surprised.

"The flat's big enough for the two of us," Susan said when I told her. She was delighted, though for some reason it took me a week before I could tell her. Then I packed my clothes, took a few books and closed the door of the house behind me.

But I told Willie Vincent the day after it happened. I got home from the office about eight. The house felt uncared for somehow, though they'd only been gone a few hours. And Henriette wasn't there busily fussing, which was a relief.

Usually I liked being in the house by myself. Not that I liked the house; it was too big, an ugly Victorian building. There were too many rooms and they were all too cold in the winter and too hot in the summer. But this evening I couldn't afford to be alone. I had been busy all day and the ruin of my personal life had been pushed out of my mind, more or less successfully. I had had a headache but that was my only conscious acknowledgment that anything had changed.

But now that I was by myself, again I had the curious feeling that the seals were falling off the passage I had blocked in my head. So I went to see Willie Vincent.

Fifi let me in.

"Hullo Fifi," I said.

She replied with a smile. She was wearing pink trousers and a tangerine sweater. The effect was rather odd.

Willie came out of the room scratching his chest. "Hullo Bill," he said casually, "how nice to see you. Come in, we're just going to eat." And he led me into the kitchen. There was no need to pretend that I had eaten. There was always enough food in Willie's house to feed any strays. The difficulty was to get it down.

After the meal, he took me back to his room.

"I'm leaving Mary," I said abruptly.

He undid the buttons of his check shirt and did them up again. "What about the children?" he asked.

"Mary thinks they'll be better off without me living in the house."

"You mean she *wants* you to go?" He seemed surprised.

I didn't answer for a bit because I didn't know what to say. It wouldn't have made sense to have said:

"I told her I would leave but I wanted her to tell me not to go and she didn't. So now I have to go."

Eventually I said, "Yes," not because it was true but because it was truer than saying "No."

"You're making a mistake Bill," he said a moment later. "I don't like Mary any more than she likes me. And for my own sake I've always been sorry that you married her. But you're tied to her now in more ways than you know. You'll do yourself no good by leaving her."

"I'm afraid it's too late," I replied. "We've agreed to break up."

"Are you going to live with Susan?"

"I think so," I said.

"That's another mistake," he said quietly. "I'm surprised you don't see it. Remember what your friend Proust says? 'A woman one loves rarely suffices for all our needs, so we deceive her with another whom we do not love.' That's dead right. You can have an affair with Susan while you're living with Mary. But if you leave Mary, for Christ's sake don't go and live with Susan." His voice tailed off. Then he said, "You don't love her anyway," and he looked at me fiercely: "Do you?"

"No," I answered dutifully.

"And you do love Mary, don't you?" He was pursuing me as I had pursued Diggins and so many more of our breed and the thought of it, each of us, dog-like, chasing our own tails without realising what we were doing, made me laugh. And I laughed for a long time, long enough to avoid answering the question.

If Willie thought it peculiar that I'd laughed at his question, he didn't say so. He leaned back in his chair, stretched out his feet and put his hands through his braces. He was limbering up to start again. I wasn't ready yet, so I got in first.

"You've been reading a lot of Proust since Fifi's been here," I said smoothly.

He stared: "What's Fifi got to do with Proust?"

"I asked you that a month ago," I complained.

"Haven't you noticed the difference since Fifi came?" he returned.

I examined him. He was wearing a different shirt but the same braces as when I'd last seen him. I looked around the room. It looked exactly the same, heavily, stridently, almost suspiciously masculine. "Can't say I have."

He nodded his head in the direction of his desk. I got up and then I saw there were two framed quotations where there had previously been only one. The new one read: "Credo quia impossibile."

I could hardly believe my eyes. This hackneyed nonsense! "You don't believe because it's impossible Willie," I cried. "What's the idea of sticking up this ham theology?"

"It's not ham," he replied patiently. "It's Tertullian and it's not my theology. It's Fifi's."

"Does Fifi know that Tertullian also wrote other rather extravagant things and in particular that he wasn't very nice about women? I seem to remember," I said, "that somewhere he described woman as a temple built over a sewer."

"I believe she does," he murmured. "I told her that he referred to women as the gateway of the devil." He reflected for a moment. "She didn't seem very concerned," he went on. "Actually she referred me to St. Bernard."

I didn't take up the reference. Instead I lay back in my chair and thought about it. What was Willie doing with this rubbish on his wall? And why show it to me?

"Anyway," I said at last, "the French don't go in for that sort of hocus-pocus, surely?"

"She's not French. She's a Swede."

"Oh yes," I said weakly.

He seized the initiative again but changed his tactics. He became very gentle and protective.

"Look here, Bill, I've said this to you before, but really I find it quite hurtful sometimes to watch you romping about with such eager zest looking for God. That's why I wanted you to look at that text. I only put it up for your benefit. It's all right for Tertullian and I dare say it's all right for Fifi to believe if it's impossible, but you believe because you think it is possible. And that's intolerable because it isn't. And you should know by now."

"I'm afraid," I replied, "that I have no idea what you're talking about."

"You look for God in people," he replied, "that's what I'm talking about. You don't seem to have realised that all living is a compromise and that you must put up with people as they are. You think your marriage has failed. Nothing of the kind," and he waved his arm airily to dispose of that possibility. Then he grinned: "There was once," he said cheerfully, "a famous incident in a large catering firm. The kitchen staff were breaking an enormous number of a certain size of plates. The management suspected grave psychological difficulties, so they called in a team of experts to make a complete analysis of management-worker relationships." He waited a moment before pronouncing the dénouement. Then he said with delight. "Do you know what the findings were? The bloody plate racks were too narrow." And he roared with laughter.

But after a moment he grew serious again. "And that's your trouble Bill," he said earnestly. "You've asked too much from Mary. That's all. Why can't you remember that she's like the rest of us, a weak soft and corruptible woman? You're prepared to recognise the human failings of your clients, why not of your wife? Yet you've sought in her impossible values and when she falls down, you think the world's come to an end. And let me tell you this, while I'm on the subject," and his voice had sharpened. "You've got no business to expect of other people, any other people, the standards you demand of yourself. If you've got high standards and you live up to them, be grateful, but be humble also. You don't live up to them because you want to, but because you have to, because if you don't, you feel uncomfortable. So you keep to your code as a matter of personal convenience and not for any other reason, whatever you may privately tell yourself. Anyway that's your affair."

I shifted in my chair. He was glaring at me as he went on. "But you've got no right to force your code on other people, neither on Mary nor anybody else. You don't professionally, why do you matrimonially?" And he grinned, suddenly jovial again.

I said mildly: "I didn't know that I did, Willie."

He gestured violently: "Didn't know! Just look what you've done to that woman of yours."

I fought back: "How do you know what I've done? You haven't seen her for ages."

"I don't need to see her," he replied leaning back comfortably in his chair, controlling the situation, "I can tell from seeing you."

I couldn't argue that. I'd done it too many times myself with other people. He returned to his theme:

"Look here Bill, if you must have God and it appears that you must, why don't you look in the right place and leave the rest of us alone?" He paused. He wanted me to be sure to understand and his voice softened as he interpreted for me: "And when I say God, I don't mean any of the tribal gang. I mean whatever it is that you look for, your values, the particular truth you seek or if you like, the highest value of all, your loyalties."

"Loyalty, Willie," I said, surprised, "a higher value than truth?"

"I think so," he replied simply.

I wanted to think about that, but he wouldn't let go:

"You may have been misled because people sometimes look like God. But you should have grown up by now. They may be beautiful, intelligent, cultured, but that doesn't prevent them also being pitiful, vain and sometimes rather squalid. And that you won't have."

I broke in just to stop the flow of words. What was he talking about? I spent my life seeing people just like that, pitiful, vain and squalid. But no exceptions he meant, no special dispensation for the people one loved and banked on—they also, Mary also, they were all like that. And if you wanted more, you had to go to God. That's what he was saying. And I didn't want to hear it. So I told him what Mary had said about Vingtot.

"You're saying what Mary said last night. She said there weren't any wonderful people, but just people who were mostly obligations anyway."

"And she's right," he replied. "You've got star dust in your eyes. It's perhaps not a bad thing in your job, but you oughtn't to allow it to destroy your family. You'll have to get your priorities right," he said pungently. "Why can't you just be a father and husband and stop being a great big warm womb for suffering humanity to return to? Why can't you leave the Universe alone? It exists by your patronage. It's entitled to a certain constraint on your part. But you want to make everything good for everybody, don't you?" he said, sneering: "You want to make it all fair.

That's because you're a bloody God seeker, because fairness only makes sense if there's a God. Take God away and it's useless to expect fairness. People just aren't fair until they get out of the race. And then fairness doesn't arise because they've ceased to be involved." Then he said wearily: "Why don't you learn to take yourself and everybody else a bit less seriously. It's not all that important." And for a moment he was quiet.

"Suppose," he went on more gently, "suppose you became a little less committed? Suppose you limited your requirements? Couldn't you shrug your shoulders at what goes on, just a little more, instead of always rushing in." He paused and said rather sadly: "I'm afraid Bill, that it's all pitched in a much lower key than you think."

He broke off abruptly and then as if it were irrelevant, he said:

"You know Michael Ayrton's work?"

"I've seen some of it," I replied.

"He says it better than I do. You look at his people, lonely, forlorn and unfulfilled, no God in those people." He broke off and shrugged. "And that's how it is for everybody."

I was flippant. I had no idea what he was talking about.

"You're a bit off your beaten track, aren't you Willie? Does all this Slav melancholy also come from Fifi?"

He looked at me for a long moment and then he decided. He got to his feet and took a piece of paper from his bureau.

"I will read you a poem," he said.

I was surprised and rather touched. I didn't know Willie wrote poetry and I was pretty sure he would have preferred me not to know. He was taking a lot of trouble with me. It occurred to me that he was trying to do for me what he complained of me trying to do for other people. But I put it aside. This was not the moment.

"It's called," he said, giving me a hard look: "On Growing Up."

I settled back in my chair while he read each line slowly. As he read, the words took shape in my mind. He knew all right. And he knew not only for himself; he knew for me also. Nor was it only that his anguish was formulated nor that it embraced mine. The poem was the Law for all Willies everywhere. It was Willie universalised.

The room which contains my life,
Is not mine; it is on loan.
The life which contains my room
Is not mine; it is let to me
On terms which I do not dictate
But accept—
If I would be happy.
There are no others available to me.

Housed as I am, insufficiently facultied,
Ineffectually talented,
Upon whom may I sup
But my like?
There are no others available to me.

The question's fragility
To which is no answer.
Is life like this?
The emptiness of the bloated need
Self-fertilising,
And sterile.

Birth is dark peaceful butchery.
O the anguish of growing!
And knowing
That for me,
This is the best that there is.
There is no other available to me.

I accept—
And withdraw my conditions.

So there it was, staring me in the face. Would I or would I not accept the terms of my life? So much I had; if I accepted and asked for no more, I could be happy. Otherwise no happiness; and there was no more to be had anyway, not by me. The terms on which I had been given the loan of my life had been fixed long since. And from that tribunal, there was no appeal.

He had made his case. All he had to do was to let me absorb it and I would be his. But like so many advocates, he couldn't bear to stop now that his point was home and as they so frequently do, he did; he blurred the edges and rubbed away the effect.

He got up from his chair and began to pace the room with long loose strides. I had only seen him do this once before and that was on the night I had told him that his decree had been made absolute. And he began to talk about his life and his marriage, not in his usual manner, impersonally as if it had happened, was happening to somebody else he knew very well, but with brutal directness.

He went on for what seemed like a very long time and then he said:

"I can't remember the last time I talked like this, Bill. The things I've just said are not things to be spoken of. Everybody has to come to terms with himself on one level or another, but it's a private, a silent process." He grimaced. "Though as you will come to discover, no cry of agony can be more dreadful than the silence of which I speak. And in the last resort, nobody can really help you to come to terms, perhaps can't even understand your need." He paused and turned to look at me.

"There are," he said, jerking the words at me, "things inside me with which I've learned to live, but only because I had to. Some of them were ugly, and I hated myself because of them. But they were all part of me and had to be accepted. I didn't like myself very much and I used to think that as I would only attract my own kind, I was never going to like anybody. Everybody to whom I was attracted would dislike me as much as I disliked myself, and I could see myself living like a pariah, fearing my like and hating it all." He went on striding about the room:

"I was of course postulating an impossible situation, but you see how acute the conflict inside me must have been. And when Joan went, I knew I had to make the peace with myself somehow. I had to learn to accept what I was."

He stood sombrely in front of me.

"And you'll have to do the same, Bill. You also will have to grow up. You'll have to learn how to make your own relationship with yourself a good one." He looked at me quizzically. "You know, I suppose," he said, "that you do have a relationship with yourself, don't you? And that if it isn't working properly, that some part of you will always be at odds with the other, wearing you down and tiring you out?"

He paused, not to allow me to speak, but to find the words that would penetrate. "It's all a question of identity," he said eventually. "The problem is 'Who are you?' and by that I mean the face behind the labels which you and I and everybody else wear. You have to recognise who you are and when you've done that, you've got to learn to reckon with it. I'm not sure which is harder or which is worse. And all anybody can do to help is to point out the question. The answer you must find for yourself," and his voice trailed off as he sat down heavily.

I was quite out of my depth. I wasn't sure whether I knew what he was talking about or not. And for a long time there was silence between us.

Then he got up and took out some bottles of beer and glasses from a cupboard. He poured the beer and gave me my glass and silently we played chess until once again I found myself relaxed and my head quiet.

As we finished the third game, I said, "Thank you for your advice Willie and thank you particularly for the poem."

"What are you going to do about Mary?" he asked.

I shrugged: "What can I do?"

He looked at me full in the face, suddenly furious:

"Are you just going to let her go?"

"She's gone, I tell you," I said angrily.

"You bloody fool. Are you telling me that a woman takes her two children and runs away from her husband for no reason? And that the husband is entitled to shrug and bleat that he doesn't know what to do?"

I was too tired to be angry any more:

"What does it matter what the reasons are? She's gone and that's that."

Willie was quiet again: "You gave Mary nothing and you demanded of her more than anybody has a right to ask. That's why your marriage has broken down, if it has broken down. And if it hasn't, then the remedy is in your hands."

I found this rather disquieting. Mary had said the same sort of thing several times.

"It's funny you should say that Willie. Mary's said it too. How is it that it's obvious to everybody but me that I didn't love my wife enough?"

"It isn't obvious to everybody," he replied. "Most people think you're a good husband and that Mary's a bitch. As a matter of fact, I should think she's had a pretty thin time, one way and another, hasn't she Bill?"

I looked at him: "Why do you say that Willie?" I could hear Mary's voice in my ear echoing the last words he had used:

"You've had another life, haven't you?" he said. "And I don't mean Susan. I mean your job. But what's she had? She could say what Victor Hugo said:

" 'Emporte le bonheur et laisse-moi l'ennui.' "

"Why don't you get Fifi to stick that up over your desk as well?" I said sourly.

"Because Fifi doesn't expect from me what you'd led Mary to expect of you," he said in reply. Then he grinned. "I believe you lawyers call it misrepresentation don't you?"

"I think I'll go," I said, "before you think of any more quotations. I've had enough for one session."

As I walked home to the empty house, I could hear my voice saying to Diggins, "You didn't love enough," but I was pretty sick of echoes by this time. If I didn't love enough, I didn't, and that was that. I couldn't do any more.

At the end of the week, after I had packed I wondered whether I should write a note to Mary. In principle I disapproved of farewell notes. I thought they were vulgar. But I wrote one just the same. One can afford a bit of vulgarity in putting an end to thirteen years living. I didn't know what to say. I didn't feel elated because I was going to be free. I didn't particularly want to be free. And I didn't feel depressed that I was leaving. I didn't feel anything. I had been rescued by my friend the stone. I was cool, controlled and dead. So I took out my pen and wrote whatever came into my head:

Home.

Dearest Mary,

I don't know what to say because I never thought this could happen to us. I have never loved anyone but you, and I do not go because I love somebody else. I go only because we both agreed that life together is impossible.

As soon as I have sorted myself out, I will telephone to arrange to see the children.

Money will go into your Bank as usual.

I hope you enjoyed your holiday.

Bill.

I put it inside an envelope and propped it against the mirror of her dressing table, feeling silly and dramatic. And then I rushed out of the house because I couldn't bear the incongruity of it, because I couldn't understand how I could turn my back on thirteen years of marriage without even a tear, because I didn't feel anything and because I should have. And because it all seemed to be happening to somebody else.

EASTER TERM

I DON'T KNOW IF I expected anything special when I moved in with Susan, but if I did, I didn't get it. She was a friendly, interested companion and comfortable to be with, except perhaps in the mornings. But she didn't strike any spark out of me. It had been a long time since I had had a continuous relationship with a woman, a long time since I had wanted to spend the evening in the same place as I had spent the previous evening and the one before that. It was nice to go home to Susan and have dinner with her instead of a book. And it was nice to feel her concern. But she was impossibly exuberant in the morning, when she behaved like one of those jolly bouncy girls who belong to suburban tennis clubs. Not that it mattered much to me. I hardly noticed it. Of the community of personalities housed inside me, the Controller never really took over until I'd been out of bed for well over an hour and by that time I was always out of the way. And she'd stopped being jolly by the evening.

She also ran the bath for me in the morning, so that when I got up, there were no dreary preliminaries to get through by myself and I could move straight from safety into luxury. I was always prepared to risk anything if it were comfortable enough.

But I began to arrive at the office early in the morning. It had nothing to do with Susan's barley sugar. It was merely a balance of convenience. On the whole, I was more seriously incommoded by a jolly breakfast than by getting up earlier. So I got up earlier. But still I didn't seem able to leave any earlier in the evening.

Easter Term is the shortest term of all. It only lasts about six weeks and not a great deal can be done in six weeks. We had four undefended divorces and a defended divorce in the List as well as a slander action in the Jury List. There were several Rent Act cases in the County Court but I didn't understand the Rent Acts and Henry handled them with Counsel's help when a tricky point turned up. The new work kept coming in and we were pretty busy.

In the first week of term, the defended divorce was heard. We were acting for the wife Petitioner who alleged adultery and desertion and the husband Respondent was cross-petitioning for divorce on the ground of cruelty and desertion. It lasted three days. As I listened to the conflicting evidence on almost every material issue, I wondered why the husband was bothering. They both wanted a divorce. There was no question of maintenance, because the wife wanted to re-marry as soon as she got a decree. The husband must have been advised that this cross-petition might so weaken both cases that in the end neither of them would get a decree and that the costs would be correspondingly increased. But he fought his wife bitterly on every point. In the end he won. The Judge gave him a decree and rejected his wife's story. He then had the privilege of paying her costs and his own. The wife didn't seem to mind much.

I remembered having thought how flat and passionless undefended divorces were, but defended cases like this one really were a battlefield. And they lacked dignity even more than undefended cases. Butchers' shops wouldn't have helped here. For all practical purposes by the end of the second day, the Court was a butcher's shop.

But the slander action was settled. We were acting for the Defendant and he was pretty certain to lose. It wasn't a very interesting case and I had been drawn in because he worked in a garage with a man I'd known in the Army.

He had called a shopkeeper called Mrs. Smith a twister and several people had heard him. He assured me that she really was a twister, that he knew plenty of people who would give evidence and gladly say so and that anyway she would never dare to go into Court.

I'd heard this kind of thing before, but people just don't like going to Court to be witnesses. And that's what I told him. But he wouldn't believe it. He was confident he said, that he would find the necessary evidence.

Well he didn't and one day we found ourselves almost on for trial.

People are odd. I'd said to him at the beginning that it seemed to me his best course would be to offer a humble apology and if Mrs. Smith accepted it, he'd be out of the mess at little cost. But this he wouldn't do. He wanted to fight her, he said and he would spend his last penny to do it. When it actually came to his last penny, he didn't want to spend it at all and he instructed me to do the best I could without paying anything. By this time considerable costs had been incurred and I didn't know at all how Mrs. Smith was going to be persuaded to accept just an apology.

By a lucky accident I ran into the solicitor acting for Mrs. Smith just as I was leaving the Court one day. I knew him very slightly.

"Hello Mortlock," he said cheerfully. "This is fortunate. I was going to telephone you about my Mrs. Smith."

"What about?" I said guardedly. There could be a dozen reasons why he should want to talk to me about the case. Only one of them might be to settle, though Plaintiffs did notoriously get cold feet as their cases neared trial. It was as well to be cautious.

"Have you got time for a coffee?" he asked.

"I've got a few minutes."

And we went into the Kardomah.

He was a very fat man and he held his belly up as he put his bottom into the chair. Then he dropped his belly into place and moved to the attack. I had the fancy that he lowered his head, but this may have been imagination.

"You've got no defence of course," he said brusquely.

I began to laugh. "Have you invited me here to tell me that?" I asked.

He frowned, wearing the ponderous expression you sometimes see on the face of the Adjutant bird, though there the resemblance ended. Then he made an effort and stopped frowning.

"No, of course not," he said. "I was wondering if you and I could get together. It seems rather a silly case to fight."

This was better. "Well," I replied, "you know I'm always ready to listen. What are your ideas?"

"I think I could persuade my client to accept £200," he said earnestly. "And you'd have to make an apology in open Court and pay the costs of course."

I began to laugh again, this time with more design.

He didn't take ridicule, even on a small scale, very well. The pattern was repeated and he began to frown.

"I'm sure you could persuade her," I agreed. "And she'd be

well advised to be persuaded. Because she won't get £200 from a Jury."

"Yes, but you've got no defence man," he pressed.

"You don't think I'm going into Court on that defence?" I asked.

"I suppose you're going to try and justify," he said. "But you won't get leave at this stage. It's too late."

He pressed his lips tightly together. He was worried just the same. Almost certainly he feared a plea of justification, that we might call witnesses to give evidence about Mrs. Smith's crooked shopkeeping. He couldn't know that we had abandoned this hope. I was reluctant to bluff too far; yet on the other hand he might be proposing to throw in his hand. I decided to take a chance.

"All your woman wants is an apology, doesn't she? She only wants to show it to the neighbours in the local paper. Isn't that so?"

"Well," he said grudgingly.

"I'll try and get you a really good apology," I said enthusiastically. And then just in case he got ideas above his station, I said more sombrely, "Mark you, my chap will take a bit of persuading at this stage. And I can tell you he won't pay a penny in damages and he won't pay your costs. But he might just agree to an apology. If you're interested in this offer, you'll have to give me a quick decision because we've got to get on."

I tried to say just enough to suggest that we were going to get on with amending the Defence to plead justification, without actually saying so. He took the point and nodded.

He telephoned me the next day. Mrs. Smith would accept an apology made in open Court if the Defendant would pay £25 towards her costs. She agreed not to ask for damages.

My client was a nice man, reasonable, sensible and intelligent. He also understood very well the position he was in. Yet I had the greatest difficulty in persuading him to pay the £25. He knew Mrs. Smith would be considerably out of pocket, that in a sense he had beaten her, but still he was reluctant. And it's a common enough complaint by solicitors that the most reasonable of men becomes as stubborn as any mule the moment he gets inside your office. But he settled and that was the end of the slander action.

As I left the Court after the apology had been read out, I felt smug. What a fine profession I thought. I'd never known a

226

solicitor, though I dare say there may be such, who'd advised his client to continue litigation when he knew it was against his client's interests. Indeed sometimes one had to fight the man to make him see it. And the same applied to the Bar. But I didn't feel smug for long. I passed a book-shop and as I stopped briefly to look, I saw Mrs. Piozzi's Johnsoniania. I opened it at random and smiled as I read. 'I would be loath to speak ill of any person I do not know, but I am afraid he is an attorney.' As I replaced it, I saw a Coleridge glaring at me and fled. Coleridge on lawyers was altogether too much.

I was going home to Susan night after night, without ever wanting to go out. I suppose I was glad to have a home once more. The flat was comfortable and I found that I was able to read again. Susan was good about most things and life with her was restful without being happy. Sometimes I felt that my flame had gone out, but then I thought that everything else wears out, so why not me? I had no plans and I looked to no future. I had never lived like this before but it was not unpleasant. I was created every morning and I died every night. Sometimes I felt half-worried that I could turn my life over with so little apparent disturbance to myself, but it passed. And I kept away from Willie Vincent on all levels. If I wanted anything, it was only to lie fallow for as long as I could.

But I did miss the children. I hate noise but I missed theirs. I dislike untidiness but I missed theirs and I wanted their chatter and excitement and the continuity of it all.

They sent me postcards from Edinburgh addressed to the office. Mary must have guessed that I wouldn't stay at the house —but nothing from her, not even my address on the postcards. The children wrote that themselves, even Edward whose handwriting was still clumsy and unformed.

And then they began to send postcards from Ireland, most of which were taken up by tales of the sad life of the Irish donkey. According to them donkeys spent all their lives carting peat up and down the lanes of Connemara. Edward was particularly incensed and sent me a coloured postcard showing a donkey with two small hampers of peat on either side of its back. The donkey didn't look ill-used to me, but Michael who was shrewder sent me a letter enclosing a horrifying drawing he had himself made of a donkey, gaunt and covered with sores and so laden that it

227

could hardly stand. At the same time I had a short note from Mary telling me that they had all gone to her sister's cottage in Connemara and that they would be home in two weeks. This was the warning letter telling me to be gone, the Notice to Quit specifying the last date on which I could remain in possession.

I had two weeks. When I had left the house, I had taken only clothes and a few books. I knew I would have to go back to sort out the papers in my desk, in the cupboard, packed away in trunks, the relics of a marriage, some to destroy, some to take. But I didn't want to go.

ANOTHER DAY

Mary was returning on Sunday. On the Friday before she was due back, I knew I couldn't put it off any longer. If I didn't go to the house the next day, I should have to go when she was there. And that had to be avoided at all costs.

"Shall I come with you?" Susan asked.

"No, I think I'd rather go by myself." I couldn't have borne for her to have come with me.

"Then I'll go down to my parents tomorrow morning. You'll surely be finished by the evening. Why don't you come then?" she suggested.

"All right," I said vaguely. I didn't know how long it would take, nor how I would cope. What I did know was that it had to be faced alone.

Susan caught an early train. I dallied in the flat. I ate some more breakfast, I read all the newspapers down to the last advertisement. And then the telephone rang. It was a curious thing that when I had lived with Mary I had never answered the telephone. Ever since I had lived with Susan, I always answered it, almost as if I were expecting a call. But whatever it was I expected, it never came.

I lifted the receiver. It was George's voice.

"Hello George." I was surprised.

"Bill, would you and Susan like to spend the week-end with us?"

"What, this week-end?" I must have sounded a bit startled.

"Yes, why not?"

"It's very kind of you George, but I've got some things to do here I'm afraid."

"No, you'd better come to us Bill."

And then I remembered his face at the office the day before. He had hesitated before going out of my door, had passed his tongue over his lips. Then he had given me a rather calculating look, clearly decided against whatever he had thought of saying, and had gone. Now he had changed his mind. I was touched by

229

his kindness. But it also made me laugh. It was always like this. Whenever you thought you could do something for somebody, it blew up in your face. George knew Mary was coming back this week-end and he thought I was going to mope. And he was trying to help, all to no purpose.

"What are you laughing at?" he asked suspiciously.

"I'm sorry George," I spluttered, "but it's all right really. Susan's gone to her people and I'm going to the house to sort out my things. This evening I'm going down to join her."

"Oh," he said, relieved. "You're quite sure?"

"Yes, I'm quite sure. But thank you just the same."

And then I faced what had to be faced.

I felt all right on the way. I even went into a butcher and bought a joint to take with me. They would be back on Sunday morning, all the shops would be closed and Mary would have forgotten to arrange for anything to be delivered. She always did. So I also bought some vegetables, some groceries and a loaf of bread to keep them going.

And I felt all right when I got into the house, even when I went into my own room. It wasn't until I started to rummage through the papers that I began to feel sick in the pit of my stomach. But there was nothing to do except get drunk or put up with it. And if I got drunk I should have to stay drunk until I went to Susan's family. So I decided to put up with it.

I cleared my desk and the cupboard and put aside the papers I wanted. By this time my back was nearly breaking and I straightened up for a moment before I got on to the last trunk. There I came across some old letters which Mary had written when I had been abroad in the Army. I hadn't thought of those letters since I had packed them away, years and years ago. I couldn't even remember why I had kept them. I had destroyed all the others. I began to search for the rest of them until I had collected all there were, twenty-one in all.

I held the letters in my hand for a long time wondering whether I should read them or destroy them unread. And then without having made any decision, I saw my fingers take a letter from its envelope.

You've been away now darling a year and eighty-four days. I thought when the time came for you to go that I should never be able to go on living because I knew then as I know now that there is no purpose, no point in life if I do not share it with you.

It seems to me so curious that once I had a separate existence—before I knew you. But I can no longer think back to what it was like then. And I cannot, dare not, do not want to think of an existence in the future which doesn't include you as the centre.

I am so looking forward to the day when we shall be together for ever darling, when we need never be parted for a single night. And thank you so very much for writing me so often. I know it isn't easy for you to write. But I so love the warmth in you which communicates to me almost like a physical thing. And when I touch the paper on which you wrote the words I read, so many thousands of miles away from me, the pleasure in my finger-tips passes over my whole body. And then I am aflame for you. But this too can wait.

Sometimes, as I dust an ornament or pick up a book, I catch my breath as I remember an occasion when you touched them too. And then I come to myself having gloriously dreamed away a separating hour. And it is then that I feel most especially near to you.

Does this sound gauche? It is my solace.

Darling, I should like to say this to you. I want only to be with you. I don't care if I never see anyone else except you and our children. I will do whatever you want. I will live wherever you say. I don't care what job you do and whether you're good at it or not. I don't care how much money we have. All I want is your love. But that I absolutely must have. If I am loved by you, I am content, more than content, because I will have the whole world.

Sweetest I know you love me. But tell me. Tell me in every letter. And then I will wait as patiently as I can for the War to be over.

And for my part, I tell you darling, though you have read it in every letter, that I'll love you all my life and longer if it's at all possible. I will make you so happy that you will know always that no man was ever so well loved.

And now I shall creep to bed to dream (I hope) of you.

Darling if you lived as long as Methuselah (and I did too)

231

still it wouldn't be long enough for me. I will love you for ever.

Mary.

When I had read the letter, I put it carefully back in its envelope with mechanical fingers. Now I knew why I had kept them, so that I could always know that no man was ever so well loved.

I went on reading, compulsively. I hardly knew what I was doing. I felt crumpled inside and hurting all over my outside as if my skin had suddenly grown too tight. This time the seals had really been wrenched off. I could feel the curtains inside my head being swept open in one brutal movement, and the years which had gone and which I had so completely forgotten came rolling back like big breakers washing over me until I was bruised and dazed; and all the time the awful sickness lurching inside me. A phrase from Schubert's Unfinished Symphony formulated itself and shivered through me. How could I have forgotten all this? But I had. Completely. And the music reverberated through me.

And then I began to cry, sobbing bitter hopeless tears, as a child does, quite out of control. And for the rest of that terrible day, I walked up and down the room, up and down, and I wept without ceasing.

And then I could weep no more. I sank into a chair exhausted, and surveyed the room and the ruin of my life. Willie Vincent's poem came into my head and I repeated the lines aloud. I felt a dull surprise at hearing my voice. I was no good at learning things by rote, but this poem I knew by heart. Now I saw what I had done, but I could not see how it was to be undone. I began to curse myself for my stupidity, for my pride, for my lack of understanding, for having forgotten. I had forgotten what it had been like to be happy. And I began to weep again, choking with self-pity.

Until I took myself in hand. I couldn't go back to Susan now. That was over. But what could I say to Mary? That I was sorry, that I wanted to make a new start? She'd wanted to make a new start the night before she left, and what had I done? I had been the outraged husband. Who is your lover, I had wanted to know, as if it could have made any difference. But I had wanted to know. I had wanted a weapon. And then I saw it so clearly that I almost laughed. I had behaved in exactly, but precisely the way my clients behaved. They would take their wives back if they said sorry, if they could be purified. But they had to be right and the wives had to be wrong. I stared at myself, aghast. I was like all the rest, worse than them; because despite all I knew for them, I knew nothing for myself. I hadn't even seen it when Willie Vincent had stuck it under my nose. And George knew too. That's why he'd telephoned. Only I, only I hadn't known. And how often had I said to other people surveying their private disasters in my office: "Life must go on." Now I said it to myself and it didn't work. I didn't want my life to go on.

All these years Mary and I had lived together. How often had she not reminded me of the happiness we'd once had? And I had waved it away, had forgotten, had other things to do. Until she'd stopped trying to make me remember and began to defend herself, helped us to destroy each other. And now when she'd learned how to do it, I wanted to stop it. I wanted to put it all right. I wanted us to be as we used to be, before we'd started to cut each other in pieces. And still it wasn't enough for me humbly to offer to sew the pieces up. Even now I insisted on a magical rebirth. I didn't want just to start again. I wanted to wipe out all the ugliness, wipe off all the filth between us. We had to be clean again. I started to laugh and tears ran down my face. My God, after all the things I'd said to other people, after all the philosophy, all the pompous high sounding talk, the wise counsellor and friend of the people turned out to be only a puppet, pulled by exactly the same strings, on exactly the same terms, with no discount for being in the trade himself.

I lay back in the chair dully. Where was the magic switch? I had always thought there was a switch, if only one could find it and find it in time. And then unbidden, there crept into my mind the recollection of my form-master at school taking us for mathematics one day and explaining the concept of the square root of minus one. The whole idea had been meaningless to us and perhaps to enliven a rather boring lesson he told us of the brilliant mathematician who had spent his whole life on this problem until he had finally gone mad and been carted off to an asylum. I hadn't thought of that no doubt apocryphal story from the time it had been told until now, but now I couldn't get it out of my head. All I could see was the madman's face poking between the bars of his cell, his unkempt grey hair falling over his bloodshot eyes, his hands gripping the bars, skinny hands with thick blue veins rolling drunkenly over the backs. And I could hear his thin triumphant voice shrieking along the passage: "I've got it I tell you. I've got it. It's the square root of minus one." And the warder opposite the cell leaning against the wall, was grinning.

So even finding the switch was no answer. And the madman disappeared, but he might just as well have stayed. I could see now that all the years of our marriage divided Mary and me. I could think of nothing but what had been. She would know only what was. Madness might have been a relief; at least it would be recognisable for what it was. Mary and I were two ghosts, wandering in different planes of time, able to hear but not to touch, two voices speaking different tongues. And utterly without communication.

And then finally I knew I was finished. But as the tears again pricked my eyes, contempt for myself awoke. I'd done with weeping. I had wept more this day than I had wept since I had been twelve, when I had privately decided that only babies cried, babies being boys under twelve. And I moved from contempt to ridicule and sneered at myself as the central character of a preposterous melodrama. Could anything be more absurd than a sober London Solicitor crying over a few mouldering pieces of paper? Could farce be taken to greater limits than for the same sober individual to make himself believe, even for an instant, that the emotions which had existed over ten years earlier could be re-awakened by moving the reference back? And really could any cheap comedy be more corny than the theme of a dead love revived by the accidental discovery of a few old letters, not even tied together with a ribbon. Almost I could have laughed. Almost, but not quite, because melodrama, farce or cheap comedy, it was all true and it had happened to me.

I got out of my chair. It was time to go. In this room my life remained suspended. And that was no good. It had to go on because it couldn't go back.

As I began to collect the papers I wanted to take away with me, my eye fell on the parcels of food I had bought and I took them into the kitchen. It was only when I opened the door of the refrigerator that I remembered it wasn't working. Mary hadn't had time to get it fixed before she went away. Or that's what she'd said.

I thought I had better half-cook the meat before I went. It would only mean another half an hour or so to wait. I put the meat in the oven, turned on the gas and sat down. I was too tired to read, too tired to do anything but sit.

AND AFTER

THEY TOLD ME in the hospital that I had forgotten to light the gas. They looked as if they meant it too. They said that I had been saved twice over.

Mary had written asking Henriette to get some food in for her. I had never known Mary do this before. Henriette had dutifully done the shopping and had intended to bring it to the house in the morning. But what with one thing and another, she'd been held up and hadn't arrived until well after dark. She'd found me lying on the floor of the kitchen, with the joint in the oven and the gas turned full on.

But apparently I should have been saved even without the good and so much maligned Henriette, because while she was still shrieking, George arrived and dragged me into the air. He told me later that he hadn't liked the sound of my voice on the telephone and had been worrying all day and eventually he'd telephoned first the flat and then the house without reply. So he got the car out and drove to the house.

I smiled to myself as soon as I was able. At least it hadn't been bogus. Whatever plans my Controller had had for my disposal, they had been honest. It was not knowable that Henriette and George would arrive in the nick of time. And then I smiled a counter-smile. Nothing had changed. A prig to the last, even now I had to be sure that I had behaved properly, honestly, with no fraud.

It was comfortable to lie back amid the white sheets. And I lay for what seemed a long, long time. Mary came and sat by the bed and while she was there, some of my friends also came. I felt emptied in body and spirit though I didn't appear to have lost any weight.

It was some time before I was able to work. When I got back to the office, George said that he thought we ought to get another partner, because we'd both been carrying too much of a load, particularly me. It might make a bit of difference to our income he said, but if the new man were any good, it wouldn't be for long. Also he added, looking at me as if he expected me to object, he thought I should give up divorce and concentrate on the other side of the work with him. I didn't object.

And life with Mary was easy now. We didn't talk much, but she was gentle with me as I was with her and at week-ends the children made remarkable models with the Meccano set, now added to until it seemed to have every part ever made. And I watched without envy things come to life almost beyond belief.

I didn't think of Susan at all. George told me one day at the hospital when I was almost better, that he had seen her and explained everything and that my clothes and things were back at the house. I don't know what he explained to her but she never came to the hospital.

But until we found another partner, I had to get on with the work currently pending and so one morning not long after I had returned, I found myself once again in the Divorce Court. As I relieved Henry and sat down, I saw that the Judge appeared to be horrified:

"But this is brazen, Mr. Newing," he was saying. "At the very moment when the Petitioner was signing her discretion statement, she was living in adultery and I imagine she has continued to do so. You'd better ask her."

Newing cleared his throat.

"Are you now living in adultery with the gentleman you name in your discretion statement?" he asked.

Fanny Trenchant nodded.

The Judge snorted.

Newing did what he could: "Have you any plans if you are granted a decree?"

"Yes, we intend to marry."

This was all in the Discretion Statement but Fanny was asking for her fourth marriage to be dissolved, and Judges sometimes got restive when they felt that the Court was being treated as a Divorce Agency. Still normally there would have been no difficulty but Judge Boggle was sitting, and when Henry had told me that Fanny's divorce was coming before him, I had expected trouble. And it came.

He said: "I find the Petitioner has made out her case. But in considering whether this is a case where I could properly exercise my discretion in respect of her admitted adultery, I am bound to say that I am gravely disturbed by the Petitioner's attitude. I do not think she regards her adultery as being a very serious matter."

He paused and licked his lips. I licked my lips too and I saw Fanny doing the same.

Then he went on: "But in all the circumstances I have come to the conclusion that I can properly exercise my discretion in her favour and I grant the Petitioner a decree Nisi. But I will make no order as to costs."

This meant that instead of her husband having to pay the costs she would have to pay them herself. And although her financial position was as desperate as usual, I imagined she would not be gravely disturbed by this. She was going to have a new husband and new husbands while they're new, tend to be good about money.

But Newing was cross. He took me to one side.

"Why on earth didn't you tell her to stop sleeping with that chap until the divorce was over?"

"I did."

"Well why didn't she?" he demanded.

I began to laugh: "You'd better ask her yourself," I replied and beckoned to her.

Newing clutched my arm: "No, no," he said hastily.

"Well you were lucky Fanny," I said as she came towards us, her bosom well advanced, "you nearly missed it."

"Yes," she giggled, "he was rather difficult about Roger, wasn't he?" But her eyes were shining with pleasure and anticipation.

I looked at Newing. He cleared his throat.

"Ah well," he said, "we've got the decree and that's all that matters."

Fanny and Roger came to dinner with us in the evening. Roger brought with him two very good bottles of wine to celebrate. The dinner was a jolly affair and after the table had been cleared, he said:

"I say, I hope you don't mind, but Fanny has told me such a lot about you that I wonder if I could ask you to see a friend of mine."

I looked at him for a moment. I knew what his friend would want. It was now or never. So I said:

"Does your friend want a divorce?"

He nodded.

238

"Well," I went on as sympathetically as I could. "I'm not really sure I can help him because I'm giving up divorce."

"Bill, you're not!" Fanny objected, her bosom moving towards me aggressively.

I smiled at her: "I found it got too much for me Fanny, but I'll get my Managing Clerk to see your friend, Roger if you like."

Roger's brow was furrowed. "He was rather banking on you," he said in a worried voice, "after what Fanny had told him."

I laughed. "Don't worry," I said reassuringly. "Henry is very competent and anyway I can send your friend to half a dozen Solicitors who'll look after him."

Roger was still looking worried. "I've been rather stupid," he said apologetically, "but I was pretty sure you'd take this case on," he gestured with his hands, "knowing Fanny so well and I've rather pledged you." He paused and then went on eagerly, "I only did that because this man's case is so complicated that he really does need someone first-class." His voice trailed off.

"It's really my fault Bill," Fanny came to the rescue. "I told him I was sure you'd do it."

Her voice took on the pleading note I knew of old:

"Couldn't you do just this last one, Bill. Nobody can do it so well as you. You know that."

I would have faced it out. I started to say: "That's all nonsense . . ." when Mary intervened: "Perhaps there'd be no harm, this last time darling." She smiled at me encouragingly, and I shrugged.

"All right Roger," I said, trying to smile, but my face felt like a mask and I could hardly move my lips. "Ask him to give me a ring. I'll do this last one to please you and Fanny."

But I knew as I said it that it was all bogus. I wasn't going to do it to please anyone. I was just going to do it. One doesn't escape so easily.

After they had gone and I was helping Mary to put everything away, I took the two empty bottles to throw them in the bin. As I passed her, she said absently: "Don't throw them away darling. They'll make such nice lamps."